'Where are my clothes? You must have taken them off me!' Rachel accused.

'I wasn't going to put you to bed fully dressed.' Ned tried to gather her into his arms.

'Don't you dare touch me! You shouldn't have put me to bed at all!'

Ned drew reluctantly away from her. 'Don't be stupid! I had to do something with you.'

'The stupidest thing *I* ever did was falling for you!'

'Oh, belt up!'

Dear Reader

Who are your favourite Mills & Boon heroes? We'll bet our bottom *ecu* that European men—French, Greek and Italian—will be among them. There's something unique about courtship Continental-style! Which is why Mills & Boon has launched *Euromance*—a book each month that features a gorgeous hero from one of the twelve EC countries. This month you can experience the sensual charm of the Irish, in Emma Richmond's gentle tale, LOVE OF MY HEART—look out for the attractive paperback cover!

The Editor

Jessica Marchant has travelled extensively, and has also taught English and Drama in a comprehensive school to pupils aged eleven to sixteen. Her first pocket-money at the age of five went on a notebook and pencil, and she has written ever since. She has sold many short stories and articles, but now writes exclusively for Mills & Boon. She likes writing romance because she herself married for love at the age of twenty, and is still living happily ever after.

Recent titles by the same author:

THE GREEN HEART

MIDNIGHT STRANGER

BY
JESSICA MARCHANT

MILLS & BOON LIMITED
ETON HOUSE   18-24 PARADISE ROAD
RICHMOND   SURREY   TW9 1SR

*First published in Great Britain 1993
by Mills & Boon Limited*

© Jessica Marchant 1993

*Australian copyright 1993
Philippine copyright 1993
This edition 1993*

ISBN 0 263 78015 5

*Set in Times Roman 10 on 12 pt.
01-9305-52117 C*

Made and printed in Great Britain

CHAPTER ONE

'I'M LOOKING for...I mean, *je cherche*...' Rachel cleared her throat, and tried to summon her rusty French to her tired, reluctant tongue '...Monsieur Flavell. Monsieur Nathan Flavell.'

'Monsieur Ned?' The stately lady behind the bar gave her a mildly frowning glance. 'I do not think——'

'You must be Madame Robert,' Rachel interrupted in relief. 'Ned's told me on the phone how good your English is.'

''e is very kind,' Madame Robert observed with grave dignity. 'I much regret, I cannot leave 'ere to 'elp you, *mademoiselle*...'

'To find him, you mean? That's all right, I'll manage.'

'As you see, we 'ave no reception area...'

'I'll wait here. It's a lovely bar.'

Rachel had spoken from mere politeness, but when she glanced round she found it was the simple truth. She'd been too dazed to see when she first came in, but now she could well understand why Ned would rather stay in this friendly place than in any of the luxury hotels he could so well afford. From its little plaited-straw cover down to its dark wood counter, the bar glowed. A row of silver cups glimmered among its red, green and amber bottles, flanking a group photo of what had to be the St-Jean-les-Chats brass band. The shelves were lined with looking-glass, which cheerfully reflected the one or two late customers on their high stools who had all turned with frank Gallic interest towards...

Oh, my goodness, Rachel thought as she caught sight of her own reflection. That can't be me. It just can't.

But the ravaged goblin in the mirror was wearing her own linen jacket. So this creature was herself, whey-faced and flaky-skinned, the make-up which should have brought out the blue of her eyes showing them instead cavernous with fatigue. As for her wayward dark brown hair, most of it was anywhere but in the hasty knot she had pinned up before she set out from Caster—how long ago? Her image shuddered, and looked away.

'Ned's not in, then?' she asked, thinking longingly of a hot shower and cool sheets.

'I do not know.' Madame Robert glanced towards her panel of keys, and then up the staircase. 'I . . . I do not know.'

She's stalling. The message filtered at last into Rachel's fatigue-drugged brain, and set new alarm bells ringing. Of course Ned was in—not a single key was left on that panel. For some reason of her own, Madame Robert didn't want to admit it.

So there really is something badly wrong? Rachel thought with a new emptiness in her stomach. Well, that's what I came here to find out. And I've got this far—I won't be stopped now.

She called on the last of her strength, and straightened to her full five feet six. 'I'll go up to him.'

Madame Robert's dark eyes were full of a faintly weary sympathy. 'I am not sure that would be a good idea, *mademoiselle*.'

'It's all right, I'm . . . I'm not really a *mademoiselle*.' Rachel struggled with the old problem. 'Ned's my . . .'

And here it was again. *Husband* was the word she'd nearly used, but she couldn't, because he wasn't.

She found it hard enough at the best of times to express what was between her and Ned in one word. He was everything to her, the only man she had ever wanted or ever would, but she couldn't have said that to a stranger even in her own home town. Mostly she referred to him as, 'my guy', or more formally as, 'the man I live with'—but she always hated doing that.

'...my partner,' she managed at last, miserably aware that they could have been partners in anything from a card-game to a legal practice. 'And he *is* in, isn't he?'

Madame Robert glanced once more up the stairs.

'What number?' Rachel asked.

'It is our best room,' Madame Robert said rapidly. She paused, and spoke again as if she had just thought of something new to say. 'On the top floor. Beautiful views over the town, the country.'

Rachel swayed against the counter, mastered her dizziness, and tried again. 'And he's in?'

Maybe she was still swaying. At any rate the nearest customer, a round, pink-cheeked man whose anorak smelt of farms, put out a supporting hand. She rallied, and the man murmured something across the bar, much too fast to make out.

Madame Robert didn't answer in words, but turned to the shining rows of glasses. Her next remark was delivered over her shoulder, while she selected a bottle and a small balloon glass with an advertisement on it.

'Two floors, it is too 'igh to climb.' She poured, and came back to the counter to set the glass in front of Rachel. 'Compliments of Monsieur Durand.'

The beaming farmer raised his own glass in salute.

'*Merci*,' Rachel stammered, not touching the brandy, '*mais*...' She gave up, and turned back to Madame Robert. 'Ned's room number, please.'

'But 'e is...' Madame Robert paused, expanded her lungs in the most leisurely manner, and started again with an explosive 'aitch' sound. '*He* is occupied, I think.'

'He can't be too occupied to see his...'

Damn it, here came the same problem again. Should she call herself his bedfellow? His comfort and responsibility? His friend and lover and companion in the flat overlooking the estuary? His possible wife some time soon?

Or some time never. Just when she had believed she might move Ned in the right direction, that wretched letter had arrived—was it yesterday? And now it nestled poisonously in her handbag, and must be sorted out at whatever cost.

She shouldered the bag, and prepared for a final effort. 'What number?'

Madame Robert made one last attempt. 'I do not think Monsieur Flavell will want visitors.'

'What number?'

'*Mademoiselle*,' the shrug was kind, but infinitely cynical, 'if you are wise, you will not go up there.'

'The number?'

'*Numéro six*.' Madame Robert's mouth pulled down, consigning Rachel to her fate.

'Number six, top floor. Thank you.' Leaving her luggage strewn on the red-tiled floor of the bar, Rachel dragged herself to the stairs.

The journey from Caster had been awful. First a wait in the sky over London, then the Paris flight delayed, then all flights out of Paris cancelled for reasons she couldn't understand even when the loudspeakers gave them in English. Thank heaven for the kindly taxi driver who had known which railway station she needed, and for the high-speed train about to set off for Lyon.

But, from there, the only way to St Jean-les-Chats had been a stopping train. And the ten-in-the-evening sleepiness of St-Jean station had yielded only one taxi, whose driver had demanded a surcharge 'for the late hour' before he would bring her to the Hotel du Centre. So here she was, thirty-four hours after receiving that mysterious letter, broke and exhausted and with her worst fears back in full force.

'So he won't want visitors.' She pulled herself up from the second landing by the banister. 'Well, the sooner I know why, the better.'

Room six gave straight off the top landing, under a glaring neon light which flattened and falsified every colour. Rachel knocked, the special rhythmic knock she and Ned always used together, and waited with heart thudding.

'*Va-t'en*,' a feminine voice instructed from within.

Rachel stared at the door's white number, hoping she'd got it wrong. But how could she, when this was the only door in sight? And Madame Robert had definitely said 'top floor'. So a French girl really had called out, 'Go away,' from inside Ned's room.

Rachel was just about to knock again, hard this time, when the door opened a few cautious inches. And here he was, blocking the opening and staring down at her. His blue eyes were narrow and steel-coloured under the harsh neon, and his long mouth pulled in tight with— horror? Resignation? Perhaps a bit of both.

'Rachel.' The deep voice was distant, arid, anything but welcoming.

Rachel blinked back tears of weakness and tension. He should already have been crushing her in one of his bear hugs, pushing back her hair the better to see her face, demanding to know how she had got here, telling her how clever she had been to manage the journey all on her own. Through the weary hours she had fought back her dread of how it might really be, and now it had turned out worse than the worst she could have imagined.

'I th-thought I'd better come here myself,' she quavered, 'and see what's going on.'

'Why...?' He swallowed, hard. 'Where did you get the idea that anything's going on?'

'Oh, come on, Ned. D'you take me for a complete fool?' Struggling against the black-red haze which threatened to engulf her, she tried to push the door further open. 'You might as well let me in. I had to find out some——'

'No!' From his own side of the door he pushed it against her, keeping her out. 'You can't come in here.'

Rachel gave up and leant against the wall, squeezing her eyes tight shut. Somewhere beyond the singing darkness the door opened wider, then closed, leaving him out here on the landing with her. The old, never-failing response shivered through her, telling her that her only love was near.

She opened her eyes, and weakened at once. He was completely at a loss, found out in flagrant unfaithfulness, yet still her heart leapt as he towered over her. In the blaze of those blue-steel eyes, her blood sang as if they'd been parted years rather than days.

Or as if she were seeing him for the first time. This always happened to her, whenever she considered those hard features, the height of him, the fair hair curling from his high forehead round his fine-moulded cheekbones and flicking up from his strong neck. Even now, she couldn't believe she'd lived with this man and made him her own for two years.

Made him her own. That would have been funny, if it weren't so miserable. She looked down at the long, capable hands which should already have drawn her close.

'What've you got there?'

'This?' He raised the dark green velvet with its bands of lacy white—could they be cuffs, a collar? 'Just some rubbish that got into my room. I'd forgotten I was holding it.'

He crumpled it savagely into a ball, then jumped round and stared in disbelief. The door had opened again, to reveal an erotic vision made flesh.

'Come back, Ned.' This time, it was in charmingly accented English. 'I 'ave made myself ready, and now you keep me waiting.'

By making herself ready, the vision presumably meant stripping herself naked. Rachel stared at the wide grey-green eyes and full pink mouth, both invitingly open, and felt sick. Even with all her clothes on this girl would give any man ideas. Like this, with her graceful limbs unrestrained, her dark gold hair loose to the waist, and her perfect breasts and hips tanned with never a strap mark, how could Ned possibly have resisted her?

And it was easy to see how she'd acquired that even tan. She wasn't at all put out to be caught like this. On the contrary, she drew herself up, proud as Venus.

'So this is your English lady. This is Miss Rachel Barclay.'

Rachel felt an angry flush rising in her cheeks. 'You've told her about me.'

'I've told her nothing.' Ned's eyes, steelier than ever, were directed murderously on the naked girl.

She, however, was quite unperturbed. 'I do not mind about you.'

'*You* don't...' Rachel faltered to silence.

Ned looked down at the velvet, punched his fist into it, then shook it out to its full length. Yes, it was a dress, complete with white collar and cuffs.

How he must have enjoyed taking it off her, Rachel fumed to herself, eyeing the figure in the doorway.

'No, no, I do not mind,' it went on with a delightful shrug. 'Why should I? I do not want to keep 'im forever. I do not take 'im from you.'

Rachel turned away, unable to bear any more.

'Myself, I do not mean to belong to any man. Only to——'

A lithe movement from Ned, and the creamy purr ended in a kitten-squeak of surprise. Rachel glanced back to find that the girl's entire upper half—head and body as far as the waist—was swathed in green velvet. Ned went on pulling it down, stretching it as far as it would go, yet keeping a gingerly distance from the glowing flesh beneath.

'Put it on, you little trollop,' he ground out through clenched teeth, 'and get out.'

'But Ned,' came tragically from under the velvet, 'will you not come to bed with me? I choose you as my first——'

'I'd sooner breed budgies again.' He pushed the muffled figure back into his room and slammed the door on it. 'At least they shut up when you put a cloth over them.'

'But Ned!' The door-handle rattled. 'Our night to-gezzer! My first pleasure of womanhood——'

'I'll give you ten minutes.' He glanced at his watch with cool precision. 'If you haven't got your clothes on by then, I'll put you in the street without them.'

A squeak of fear from the other side of the door showed that the threat had told. The door-handle rattled once more, then stopped.

'As for you...' The steely eyes focused for the first time on Rachel, and the dark, thick, masculine eyebrows drew together. 'What the hell have you been doing to yourself?' He slipped an arm round her waist.

Almost she could have relaxed against him as he meant her to, and let him take over. It felt so right, this beloved hand settling at the top of her hip where it fitted so exactly.

But it doesn't belong there any more, she told herself, stiffening. Perhaps it never did.

She heaved herself upright. 'Get away from me.'

'If I do that, you'll keel over.'

'No, I won't...'

She paused, struggling against her longing to yield to that familiar, sheltering arm, to let that wide shoulder cradle her weary head. How could she still need him, after what she'd just seen? No woman needed a skunk like this, least of all her. She turned away from him, and staggered against the hard coolness of the white-painted landing wall.

He moved in again. 'Which will you have, help from me or a tumble downstairs?'

'I can perfectly well——'

'Perfectly well break your neck and die proud.' He drew her close to him. 'You're all alike, you Barclays.'

It was so easy to collapse against him, to take refuge in him as she always had all her life. He was exactly the same age as her brother, five years older than herself.

Their mothers had made friends at Caster pre-natal clinic thirty-two years ago, and ever since she could remember Ned Flavell had teased and protected her, petted her and condescended to her, and guided her through all the stages of childhood and adolescence and womanhood.

'I didn't know you ever bred budgies,' she muttered, hardly aware of what she was saying.

'For a year or so, about the time you got stuck on horses.' He settled her to him, supporting her on all sides. 'I gave them up when I couldn't stand any more of their chatter.'

'They aren't you, somehow.'

'Come on, down you go.' He eased her over a step or two.

She went with him automatically, flexing her shaking legs to step after step. 'Fancy me never knowing about the budgies.'

'Just shows, doesn't it?'

'It certainly does!'

She jerked away, found emptiness where a step should have been under her foot, and swayed for a moment in a sickening void. Then both his arms were round her again, and she fell into them. She wondered vaguely, through the singing darkness overtaking her within those protecting arms, when she had last eaten. As for sleeping, she'd forgotten what it felt like.

He swung her off her feet and tipped her against his broad chest. 'Bloody hell, woman, what've you been up to?'

'I . . . I should have been here this morning, but it took longer than they said.' She lolled against him with closed eyes, revelling in spite of herself in his warmth, his strength, the huge, steady beat of his heart.

'But why are you here at all?'

To judge from the motion, he must be carrying her down the stairs. *Away* from his room. Which had a blonde French girl in it, begging him to...

'Well might you ask why I'm here!' Rachel tried to push away from him, and felt him sway perilously.

'Watch it, you'll have us both on the landing in a heap.' He held her tighter, and the downward motion continued. 'Now I know why you weren't answering the phone.'

'Don't you wish I had been!' she muttered venomously into his chest. 'Waiting like a good girl till you called. Safe at home, out of the way.'

'Flaming women!' He rounded a corner, and started the next descent. 'D'you know how long I've spent in the bar, ringing our number? I was worried out of my mind——'

'I feel your pain.'

'Last night, I kept trying till bedtime.'

'Bedtime with who?'

'Stop that!' He must have reached the ground floor; he was lowering her to her feet. 'Now stop it!'

'Why should I? It's not *me* who's cheating——'

And then the brightness of the bar blurred round her ill-treated head. The nerve of the man to grab her shoulders and actually shake her! When he stopped, she glared up at him.

'If that's your best argument——'

'I'm not arguing, I'm telling. Come on——' he laid hands on her again '—let's get you sitting down.'

She tried to resist him, but only succeeded in collapsing against him once more. A padded bench received her, and he pushed her along it so that she had no option but to slide against the wall of the little booth. She started to protest as he slid in next to her, but had to give up. Boxed in by him, she drooped between the blue-clothed table and the wall.

'I've been trying to get through all this evening, too.' There he went, so indignant—anyone might think he were the one who had the right to complain. 'I was going to come down and have another go——'

'After you'd done enjoying yourself?'

'*I was not enjoying myself*!'

She couldn't suppress a little jump of shock as he roared it out. He must have rattled all the glasses in the bar, and surely everyone was looking at them by now?

But over his shoulder she saw with relief that the bar was almost empty, and no wonder. The clock above the silver cups showed nearly midnight. Only the pink-cheeked farmer remained, massively lowering his weight from the stool under Madame Robert's interested gaze.

He's coming to protect me, Rachel thought with satisfaction, and it just serves Ned right. I hope he...

But her imagination had to stop there. She couldn't bear the thought of Ned having to fight, even for treating her so badly.

Still, she amended to herself, it wouldn't hurt if he were just...challenged a little. To show him.

But the farmer seemed every moment less like a challenger. He had now taken up the brandy she had rejected earlier, and was trundling to their table. Once there he set it before Ned, talking rapidly and gesturing at Rachel.

'*Merci*, Monsieur Durand.' Ned took time off for a brief, comradely grin, and added something Rachel couldn't understand.

'What's all that about?' she hissed.

'He says my young lady should drink this,' Ned translated. 'He thinks you need it. I told him I'd make you drink his health.'

The farmer gave a satisfied nod, raising his hand in salute. '*Bonne nuit, m'sieur-dame.*'

The door closed behind him before Rachel had her breath back. The sheer male-chauvinist piggery of it!

'I'll drink if I damn well want to,' she announced, loud enough for both remaining listeners, 'and not if I don't.'

Madame Robert responded at once, shrugging as she continued to wash and wipe. 'Very good, *madame*. May I ask where you will stay the night?'

'In my room, of course,' Ned answered as if that were the most obvious thing. 'It's a double.'

'With a girl in it,' Rachel reminded him, newly outraged.

'That was no girl, that was Claudette Grenier.' And he laughed. Well, it was more of a snort really, and a grim one, but it still made Madame Robert look up with a frown and put down the glass she was polishing.

'Excuse me, *monsieur*.' She came to stand by their table, arms akimbo. 'I think this concerns me. So it is true that Mademoiselle Grenier went to your room?'

'Spot on.' Ned turned to Rachel. 'Remember what I told you? *Madame* knows everything that goes on.'

'The whole town knows Mademoiselle Grenier, *monsieur*.' Madame Robert's dark eyes snapped with disapproval. 'And I see yesterday 'ow she look at you.'

Rachel slumped into the padded bench. So he'd brought this girl here, and no doubt gazed into her eyes while she gazed back and the whole place enjoyed the show.

Claudette Grenier wasn't the first who'd fancied Ned, and she wouldn't be the last. Rachel sometimes wondered if a woman remained in Caster who hadn't turned to look at him in the street. Some had done more, even in Rachel's presence, and at parties one or two had tried to take him over.

Until now she'd always been happy to trust him. Her cool, capable lover roundly declared one woman enough for any man. He spent his leisure time fishing, or windsurfing, or bird-watching on the estuary, or taking to pieces and reassembling his two classic cars. All were activities, as he often pointed out, where women, with their chatter and fuss, tended to leave you alone.

Well, there had to be a first time for everything, and here it was. Claudette Grenier. Too crushed even for disgust, Rachel wondered vaguely where she'd heard the name before, and gave what attention she had to the conversation over her swimming head.

'I also see that orange car, the birthday gift of 'er father,' Madame Robert went on. 'It is park outside 'ere since 'alf an hour.'

'The hussy!' Ned sounded genuinely shocked. 'So she didn't even make a secret of coming here?'

'It seems not, *monsieur*. It may be,' Madame Robert added thoughtfully, 'that she wished it to be known.'

'But why didn't you send her packing?' Ned demanded. 'You know what her father would say.'

'I could not leave the bar, *monsieur*, and she did not come in here.' Madame Robert stifled a yawn, the first sign of fatigue she had shown at this late hour. 'She took the back entrance, I think...' She paused, her eyes attracted to the stairs.

Rachel stiffened as the vision from Ned's room, modestly covered now by the green dress, came into view round the angle of the landing. Scornful as Cleopatra, demure as a schoolgirl in her white stockings and strapped shoes, the girl posed in mid-flight. Then, sure of her effect, she came on down and sailed straight for their table.

'That was a very bad thing you did to me,' she told Ned down her charmingly tilted nose. 'You should not 'ave done that.'

Madame Robert addressed her briefly and rapidly in French. She blinked, wavered a little, looked at the clock, and aimed another sally at Ned.

'I 'ave not done with you yet. Nobody does that to Claudette Grenier.'

He made one of his big gestures, as of pushing her out of his way, but it was Madame Robert who spoke again. The two women exchanged glances, a trial of force. Then the girl swept to the door and was gone.

'*Madame*,' Ned commented with amusement, 'you're marvellous. Why didn't I think of that?'

'What did she say?' Rachel asked, hating his quickness and her slowness in the language, and the way it left her out.

It was Madame Robert who replied. 'I tell her if she does not go now, this minute, I will telephone Madame Grenier.'

'Her mother,' Ned explained. 'The most I could have come up with would have been Monsieur Grenier...'

'Monsieur Grenier.' The name had at last pierced Rachel's fog. 'So that's who she is. Monsieur Grenier's daughter.'

Now she knew why the name had been so familiar. The purpose of Ned's trip had been to work out a deal with Monsieur Grenier for the whole future output of Vignobles Grenier. If he succeeded—and he would succeed—then customers of Flavell's all over the country would have a new choice on their wine lists, a wine available in no other restaurant. That was how Ned worked, how he had built up the Flavell empire over the last nine years.

'I fear she is too much for her poor papa,' Madame Robert commented with some satisfaction. 'Since she was little she could do no wrong with Monsieur Grenier. Now they quarrel——'

'They're quarrelling?' Ned interrupted, alert as ever to anything which might affect his business interests. 'Monsieur Grenier's fallen out with his daughter?'

'She believe 'erself in love. She quarrel with the young man yesterday, and *monsieur* her father believe it is over,' Madame Robert willingly informed Ned. 'But I believe not. 'e may send 'er to study art in Paris as she wishes, but *I* believe,' added Madame Robert with relish, 'that if she do not make it up with this young man, then she will go wild.'

'She's made a start on that already,' Ned commented tersely. 'Dodged into my room under my arm, and had her clothes off before you could say *Folies Bergère*.'

'Correct me if I'm wrong,' Rachel observed from her corner, 'but I had the idea you were giving her a little help with that.'

'Was I hell!' He turned on her. 'Even if I didn't have you, what makes you think I'd go for that little mantrap?'

'Maybe I noticed the way you'd just taken her dress off.'

'I was trying,' he explained as though to an idiot child, 'to get it back on her.'

She stiffened, and glared at him. 'You expect me to believe that?'

'It is true—Claudette Grenier need no 'elp to un-dress,' Madame Robert put in. 'She sunbathe so, every weekend. The men, they come for miles.'

'Sunbathing's one thing,' Ned ground out, his jaw granite-hard above the eagle nose. 'A man's room's something else.'

'Exactly,' Rachel snapped. 'I couldn't have put it better myself.'

He turned on her. 'I've had about enough of this, Jel——'

'Don't you dare call me that!'

To her rage, she found her eyes full of tears. The nickname 'Jelly-tot' had been stuck on her by her whole family while she was still learning to walk. Nobody used it now but Ned, and she only let him because he said it reminded him how sweet she was. Especially, he said, in places no one else knew about...

She sniffed, and faced him. 'I don't want you ever to call me that again——'

'Listen, you little lunkhead.' The steely eyes merci-lessly held hers. 'At least give me credit for some business sense. It's the Grenier wine I'm after, not their virgin daughter.'

'So you kn-knew she was a virgin.' The tears spilled out.

'I know what she told me. If that was true, then she still is.'

'B-because I turned up.'

'Because I won't be hassled by a spoilt brat. Nor by a hysterical, over-imaginative girl, even,' he added with cruel finality, 'when she's *my* girl.'

'Er—*monsieur*.' Madame Robert gave the impression that she was interrupting only because she must. 'We 'ave not yet settled if *madame* is to share your room...'

'I'll see him in hell first,' Rachel retorted, wishing she weren't so hemmed in by these two powerful personalities. 'I won't even stay in the same hotel as him.'

'As you wish,' Madame Robert agreed tactfully. 'But in St-Jean, there is no other.'

'What? Why didn't you say so before? Here——' Rachel turned to Ned '—let me out.'

He didn't move. 'And where will you go?'

'What's that to you?'

'You won't even get to the station, unless you walk with that lot.' He nodded at her two cases. 'The taxi packs up at eleven.'

'Oh!'

Rachel felt more tears coming and shook her head, angrily denying them. Maybe if she thought hard, they'd go away. Maybe if she got out into the spring air, walked to the station and spent the night there, on a bench? But then what about her luggage? And what would she use for money? She hadn't even taken any return tickets, only singles, because of being able to come home with Ned in his car.

She turned to Madame Robert. 'Perhaps you could let me have a room? Just for the one night?'

Regretfully, but with professional pride, the *hôtelière* pointed to the '*Complet*' sign on the bar. 'It mean full,' she explained kindly. 'There is another on the door, but perhaps *madame* was too tired to see it.'

Rachel flogged desperately at her wandering wits. 'Then perhaps I could sleep right here?'

Madame Robert shook her head. 'I very much regret, *madame*.'

Clearly she wasn't open to discussion on this. Respectable bars did not harbour young women sleeping rough.

'Here.' Ned pushed the brandy along the table so forcefully that it danced on the sides of its little balloon glass. 'Drink up.'

Rachel compressed her lips and stared down at the glimmering, tawny liquid. 'I told you, I will if it suits me.'

'It suits you.'

She wondered if her sense of smell had been sharpened by fasting. The bouquet of the brandy was mounting to her in a heady stream, a perfume of flowers eddying in and out of something else, something stronger which yet was not a smell at all. And that whatever-it-was seemed to have got into her brain already, clearing and easing.

Could alcohol affect you through your nose? She picked up the glass, warming it between her hands as Ned had taught her, and took a good long sniff over its narrowed top. Here it came again, a wave of perfume and strength.

Whatever was she worrying about? Certainly she could walk to the station, and spend the night there. And in the morning, when the banks opened, she could get more currency with her credit cards. Then she would be able to buy a ticket, bring that wretched taxi back here, and collect her bags.

It was all quite simple now. And if the mere vapour of the brandy did so much for her, what would the drink itself do?

'Careful!' Ned snatched away the empty glass. 'It isn't lemonade, you know.'

She heard the words, but couldn't take in what they meant. The brandy was exploding into her throat, then into her stomach. Then the explosion reached her head and the whole world blinked out like a turned-off television screen.

CHAPTER TWO

'I'LL NEVER catch the train now,' Rachel exclaimed in despair. 'Not with all this food to eat.'

Somehow the mountain of cake was growing all the time. And she had to eat—their whole life together depended on it, and anyway she was so hungry. But if she ate she'd never catch the train, and Ned would grow away, away, far away without her...

She woke with relief. Snuggling into the blankets, she listened to the lark rising over Kitt's field on a thread of melody, and knew everything would be all right. She didn't really have a train to catch, only her job at the Water Board, and Ned would drive her to that as usual.

He wasn't here beside her, but the fragrance of coffee drifted from the kitchen. He must have got up early as he so often did, to go in the living-room and study the estuary through his field-glasses. Turning over and pulling the pillow under her cheek, she hoped he'd see the avocets this morning.

The pillow was odd though—it wouldn't tuck in right. And the lark's song was different, too. Pretty, but different: thinner, more tweedly...

'Hear him?' That was Ned, sitting by her on the edge of the bed. 'If you get up straight away, you'll see him.'

Used to his bird-spotting enthusiasm, she kept her eyes shut and tried to make her pillow do as it was bid. 'What kind is it?'

'A redstart. What about that then? A redstart on the tree right outside our window.'

'Silly.' She screwed up her eyes and put a hand over them to keep out the light. 'We haven't a tree, not outside our window.'

'We have here. Come and look.'

Whatever did he mean by *here*? And this really was a very strange pillow, quite the wrong shape. And the bed felt wrong too, not as firm as it should be, going down too much under his weight and tipping her towards him.

It was all right though, Ned was exactly as usual.

'Missed you,' he murmured, and drew her close.

She eagerly snuffed up the lemony fragrance of his shaving-soap. His hand closed round hers to move it from her face, and here was his usual morning salute—his light, loving kiss on her mouth. Still with her eyes shut, she parted her lips to send her tongue in quest of his, prepared to drown in her usual rush of love for him.

He was wearing his best white shirt—she could tell from the silky feel of it. And here were his dear wide shoulders inside it, and down here she could unbutton it and get her hands on the marvellous spare tautness of his abdomen...

'All right.' He caressed her bare shoulders, and murmured against her cheek, 'As long as you realise it's nearly ten.'

'What?' She pushed him away and sat up. 'I'll be late.'

But her eyes opened on a bedroom as different as possible from theirs. For one thing, the morning sun dazzled back from the low slopes of an attic ceiling. For another, it went on forever, its walls retreating into endless angles and nooks.

Both its windows were recessed; that was one of the reasons for its irregularities. Before she had time to take in any more, her attention settled on the table in the middle, where a loaded tray gave out scents a person could murder for. Here they came again: the fresh coffee she had noted while still half asleep, and new bread, and some dark, richly fruity jam—it really must be true about hunger sharpening your sense of smell. She could even smell the butter, unless she was imagining things.

And she wasn't. Fully awake at last, she sat up against the hard round bolster where her pillow should have been, and pulled the sheet to her chin.

'What have you done with my clothes?'

From his place by her on the bed, he indicated the east-facing window. It was wide open, and in front of it her azure silk shirt lay neatly draped over a hard wooden chair. Her linen jacket hung from the back of another chair, her dark trousers smoothed into their proper creases across the seat.

'You must have taken them off me!' Rachel accused.

'I wasn't going to put you to bed fully dressed.' He tried to gather her once more into his arms.

'Don't you dare touch me!' She pushed him away, yesterday's humiliations back in full force. 'You shouldn't have put me to bed at all!'

He drew reluctantly away from her, and sat with his hands resting lightly on his long, muscular thighs in their fine worsted suiting. 'Damn it, Jel, I had to do something with you.'

'I'd sooner have spent the night in the street.'

'Unconscious?' he asked with an air of much-tried patience. 'You must have forgotten how you zonked out on brandy.'

'You could have made me drink black coffee or something.'

'Don't be stupid.'

'Stupid's the word.' She shook her long hair out of the way so she could glare at him. 'And the stupidest thing I ever did was falling for you!'

'Oh, belt up!'

He rose with an air of boredom and crossed to the table. And even now, furious as she was with him and half demented with hunger, she still had to follow that smooth, easy stride. She still had to catch her breath at the way the formal trousers flowed to each movement of the long legs. The formal white shirt barely masked the power of the wide shoulders, the tanned throat rose strongly to the arrogantly tilted chin, and the glinting hair, still uncombed, stood out, shaggy as the mane of some celestial lion.

'If you're just going to score cheap points——' he bent magnificently to the table, and moved things about on the tray '—we might as well get on with breakfast.'

She licked her lips and swallowed hard. She would have loved to tell him what he could do with his breakfast, but her empty stomach wouldn't allow it. As if to make sure she understood, it gave a loud rumble.

She sniffed again, tortured by those luscious smells. 'How long has it been there?'

'I've just fetched it up from the bar.' He added milk and sugar to one of the bathtub-sized bowls of coffee, and sipped. 'This is still hot, but it'll soon cool off in these wide cups. Shall I bring yours over?'

She flung away the sheet. 'I'll... I'll get it myself...'

She caught his eyes, and snatched the sheet back over her. They'd been apart for a week and, whatever he might have done with other women, something in those glinting steel-blue eyes told her she'd better not move about naked in front of him now. She might hate letting him wait on her, hate owing him the least service, but sooner that than the other things he had in mind.

'On second thoughts, all right,' she consented ungraciously. 'I'll have it over here, and then you can...turn your back, or something, while I dress.'

'Anybody would think it was all new to me.' He added milk to the other bathtub of coffee.

'It may not be new,' she snapped, 'but, as from last night, it's out of bounds.'

'It wasn't when I undressed you in the small hours.'

'Ned! You didn't——'

'Of course not, idiot.' He peeled the crackling paper from a lump of sugar, the long fingers deft in every task, however small. 'I'm merely pointing out that I could have. You were dead to the world.'

She abandoned the argument for one more immediate. 'What are you doing with that sugar? You know I never have it.'

'You need it.' He stirred the coffee vigorously, and brought it to her.

She could hardly wait to seize it from him and drink. A distant part of her noted that he was right about the sugar—her starved system welcomed the extra calories. The whole world had become one huge coffee-cup, its upper rim shutting out the sun, its milky contents glugging almost untasted down her throat and into her receptive stomach, which sent up a rejoicing gurgle.

Deeply engrossed, she was aware of Ned as a decisive presence somewhere beyond the great coffee lake. She couldn't emerge from that cup until she had drained it; even after it was empty she tipped it as high as it would go, hoping for a last few drops. The creak of the bedsprings, and the sinking of the mattress under his weight, brought her out of her trance to defend the bed.

'Get away from me!' She held the empty cup before her like a shield, resisting his attempt to take it from her. 'I didn't say you could come and sit here.'

He shrugged. 'There's nowhere else to sit.'

And indeed, the room had only two chairs, with her clothes all over both. Besides, his work at the table had produced a sliced-off section of long French loaf, cut again down the middle, lavishly buttered and jammed and waiting in all its glory on a spread-out paper napkin on the bedside table. Without her will, her hand stole out to it, only to be gently pushed down by his.

'Madame Robert does a very traditional breakfast—no plates.'

'It's all right.' She actually had to slurp, her mouth watered so. 'I'll clear up the crumbs.'

'As you like. But it'll be easier with this.' He shook out some bright piece of cloth with a flourish. 'The specially invented Flavell tablecloth-napkin-crumb-catcher.'

She looked at it, and her anger almost melted. 'But that's your favourite shirt.'

'Red checks. Just right for a French breakfast.' The steel-blue eyes held hers in mocking triumph. 'I said you'd be glad of it one day.'

She shelved that one. She'd known the minute they'd seen it in the shop six months ago that it wouldn't suit him, and had told him so. He'd gone ahead and bought it anyway, and worn it, but always over her dead body.

She'd had another go when she'd noticed him packing it for this trip. 'Nice to see you're taking that to France. With any luck, you'll lose it.'

'And with any luck,' he'd retorted equably, 'I'll be able to wear it in peace, without you nagging at me.'

'How can I help nagging? That ghastly red kills all the gold in your hair.'

'Maybe it's better dead.' And he had folded the checked monstrosity fondly.

And now here he was, sacrificing it for her comfort. How could her heart not swell with love for him as he bade her lean forward, and held it out for her to put her arms in the sleeves?

Even so, she hesitated. 'It's back to front.'

'So it is,' he commented ironically, and went on holding it.

She shrugged, and consented to be swathed in its copious folds. He fastened the collar at the back of her neck, then arranged the fullness of the shirt above the sheets to catch the crumbs. The moment it was done she reached for that glorious bread and jam, intent on lifting it to her lips without wasting a single crumb.

Only when she had it hovering under her nose did good manners assert themselves. 'Oh—er—thank you.' She nobly delayed taking a bite. 'I'll...I'll try not to make your shirt too messy.'

'Don't try too hard,' he told her from the table. 'I can always have it washed.'

She didn't answer. She couldn't—she was too deep in a haze of creamy butter, and crust that disappeared on her tongue, and jam full of blackcurrants that yielded their juice to her teeth. By the time he came back with his own section of bread, she had finished hers.

'Heavens!' He surveyed the litter of crumbs on the shirt. 'If it weren't for the butter and jam on your face, I'd say that went down without touching the sides.'

'It was gorgeous!'

She picked up the bigger crumbs from the shirt and ate them, eyeing the piece he had prepared for himself.

He was raising it to his mouth, but stopped when he caught her eye, and offered it to her.

She swallowed hard, and shook her head. 'I can't possibly take your share...'

'Why not? I ate two solid meals yesterday, and it's obvious you didn't.'

She found she had accepted without knowing it. 'Are you sure?' She stared longingly at the bread, which had somehow transferred itself from her hand to his.

'There's more. And croissants.'

'Oh. Well, then...' She tucked in.

In the end she finished the bread, and the jam, though not the butter because there was too much of it even for her. She could have eaten both the croissants too, but that would have left Ned with no breakfast at all, so she refused his when he offered it. If not exactly appeased yet, her stomach now had something to work on, and sent new waves of sleepiness through her while Ned finished eating.

She was hardly aware of his disappearing into the partitioned-off corner of the huge room. It must be a bathroom; she could hear a tap running, and here he was again with his sponge newly damped.

'Hands!'

Blinking, she held them out and let him wipe them. He performed the same service for the stickiness round her mouth, then peeled off the Flavell tablecloth-napkin-crumb-catcher and bundled it up, along with the paper napkin from the bedside table, to carry away to the bathroom. And really, it had worked very well. She couldn't see a single crumb anywhere, though admittedly she had scavenged any she could find.

'No wonder that brandy knocked you out.' The bed sank under him again as he came back and took his seat by her. 'When did you last eat?'

'I don't know,' she murmured, eyes shut, comfortably aware of the warm weight of him near her hip. 'Plastic sandwiches on the plane, I think.' She jerked awake, the mention of her awful journey bringing all her problems sweeping over her. 'It wasn't the brandy, not really. I was tired before I started...'

She floundered to a halt. She hadn't even told him about the letter, and anyway, it was the least of her worries now. She saw him reaching out to caress her cheek, and jerked her head back.

'I told you not to touch me.'

She wriggled away to the other side of the bed, and judged the distance to her clothes. Oh, dear, look how he'd arranged them for her. He had them just the way she liked them: the tights shaken out and resting on the trousers, the suede shoes side by side beneath the chair. Such tidiness didn't come naturally to Ned—how could she help loving him, when he took this extra trouble for her?

But she must forget such softening notions. What mattered now was, could she reach her clothes before he caught her? Already he had the bedclothes half off her.

She dragged them back to her chin, and stiffened her resolution with memories of Claudette Grenier. 'We've got a lot to talk about, Ned Flavell.'

'My darling——' he stroked her still-exposed shoulder '—we're in beautiful France together. Are you going to waste it fighting?'

'I don't know.' She pushed his hand away. 'I won't know until...'

She broke off. But for that scene, whatever it was, which she'd interrupted last night, she'd probably have shown him the letter straight away. They'd have discussed it, and by now she'd have been able to stop worrying about it. Her rage flared anew.

'You were certainly making the most of the beautiful French.'

'How much longer are you going to carry on about that?' He moved back from her in chill withdrawal. 'I've told you what happened.'

'And pigs fly.'

'Will you make sense, woman?' He ran his hand through his hair as he always did when exasperated, pushing its perfect natural curves into all the wrong lines.

'Be careful,' she observed maliciously. 'Fine hair like yours often stops growing at your age.'

'If it stops, it stops,' he retorted, as well he might since it didn't show the slightest sign of thinning. 'Did you chase all this way after me to advise me on hair care?'

'So that's what I did—chase after you.' Furious, she threw back the bedclothes. 'Well, I certainly caught you——'

'And now I've caught *you.*'

'Wh-what?'

But she knew only too well what he meant. After all her care, she had now presented herself to him naked. Her scarlet briefs—mere ribbons and see-through lace which he had put in her stocking at Christmas—were no defence at all.

She stared back at him, appalled by the gleam in his eyes. She didn't dare move to cover herself, or even to glance down at her unwarily exposed flesh. All she could do was wait until he decided what to do with her, and then perhaps find the strength to resist it.

Slowly, slowly, his bright head lowered to her shoulder, and his lips touched its outer curve. A hundred hot, warning arrows sped through her blood from the contact, and she jerked back from him.

'Leave me alone! I'm going to put my clothes on——'

'Not yet you aren't.'

For all her attempts to slide as far from him as possible, she was still easily within his long reach. She made a grab for the sheet, but he whipped it to the floor. She shrank to the other side of the bed, so far and so fast that she might have fallen over its edge if he hadn't sprung full-length into its middle, his greater weight rolling her down towards him. His arm shot across her belly and pulled her in until she was pinned to his side.

'D-don't you dare!' she quavered.

But it was already far, far too late. His eyelids dropped in that narrowed, appraising stare she could never resist, and his hand caressed her thigh. And oh, dear, he didn't even have to keep hold of her. The well-known fire had leapt through her at the mere warmth of his flank against hers, the lightness of his fingers on her skin.

'Lollipops,' he murmured.

She followed his gaze down to her breasts. Sure enough, their flaring tips were living up entirely to his fond pet name for them. Tight and pink and demanding, they perfectly signalled her need before he'd even touched them. And if he once did, she would be lost.

She clenched her fists, and summoned all her will. 'Please don't, Ned.'

'Don't what?' he asked innocently.

'Just d-don't, that's all.'

He knew well enough what she meant. He'd guided her endlessly through the landscapes of love, the pastures where they could linger for hours, the forests where each new step was a discovery, the cliffs where they could take off like hang-gliders, airborne in a moment.

This, after a week's separation, would be a cliff. And when they eventually tumbled down from it, what a mess they might both be in.

'Don't do this, you mean?' He brushed his fingertips lightly across her breasts.

Rachel shuddered, closed her eyes, and wet her lips with the tip of her tongue. 'D-don't do *anything*. Please, Ned...'

But she must have lacked all conviction, and no wonder. Every nerve in her body cried out for him. And that movement of her tongue had been a mistake too—it had attracted his attention to her mouth. His own lips parting, he brought them down to hers, and she only just turned her head in time. Even so, they explored her cheeks, and then her neck, and then her shoulders. Any minute they would be closing on her breast, and making all further thought impossible.

She had to do something, fast. She laid her hands either side of his head, and her resolution almost foundered in the wave of lemon scent from his hair. But it couldn't; she couldn't let it. She fastened her fingers round his ears and pulled, hard.

'You hell-cat!' He sprang back with a shout of pain, and rubbed his ill-used ears. 'What d'you think you're doing?'

'I told you not to,' she countered as she tried to wriggle away from him.

She had reckoned without his determination. One of his arms shot over her, pinning her to the mattress with both of her own arms at her side. Try as she could, she couldn't break his grip. And here it came, his mouth at her breast, his tongue curling and caressing until she could do nothing but respond with ever-renewed delight. Pulses of desire spread through her, signals to those mysterious inner regions which were already wide open and rejoicing...

Wide open! She summoned all her strength.

'Ned, listen to me.'

'Hmm?'

He had taken her other breast, though it didn't feel like that. How it felt was that her other breast had leapt to his mouth, demanding its share. She sighed, shuddered, fought down the desire to let it all happen, and moved desperately against him.

She thought she was trying to throw him off, but it didn't work like that. The contact with the dear, well-loved body, with all its memories of pleasure shared, only sapped her resistance more than ever.

I'll have to tell him, she thought desperately. It's the only way to make him stop.

'Ned, are you listening?'

'Say on,' he murmured, his voice muffled as his lips traced their well-known, well-loved track from one breast to another.

He knew she'd stopped fighting him, and he was taking full advantage. Not needing to hold her down any more, his hand moved over her, stroking her hips and belly, advancing to her thighs and settling like a conqueror on the mount between. The hidden place beneath that mount, so ready to welcome him, opened against her will to his gentle fingers, and they entered and took possession.

'Oh!' she gasped, her whole being rushing to prepare her for the heights, the swoops, the cliff's edge.

The cliff's edge and the fall, she reminded herself urgently, and summoned all her will.

'If you go on, Ned,' she almost shouted, 'we could easily have a baby.'

It worked. His fingers paused and withdrew, leaving her cold and lonely and miserable, all dressed up and no place to go. He straightened, and stared down at her with a frown.

'Haven't you taken your Pill?'

'Not for a week.'

He lingered near her a moment more, not sure whether to believe her. Then he dragged himself to the other side of the bed and put his feet on the floor.

'Bloody hell!' He turned on her, still alight with pent-up sexuality. 'And you didn't think to say a word to me?'

'I...I wanted to talk about it...'

'Some talk, with the decision already made.' He stood up abruptly. 'You'd better get dressed.'

'Don't you give me orders,' she snapped, her own longings souring within her. 'It wasn't my idea to start all that.'

'Well, it isn't mine to start a family right now. So that makes us about equal.'

'Equal!' she repeated in a fury. 'You've got a nerve! You're one partner up on me.'

'Not that again!' He strode to the window and stared out of it, the tension of their unfinished lovemaking apparent in every line of his body. 'At this time, of all times!'

'It's got to be settled——'

'It *is* settled.' He whirled on her—a huge, brilliant being with lightning-gold hair and thunder-blue eyes. 'I can take just so much of this, Jel...' He broke off to draw in a deep, ragged breath. 'I'll say it once more.' Each word dropped hard and cold and complete as a hailstone. 'I had nothing to do with what happened last night. Have you got that?'

She clutched her arms across her nakedness, afraid of what she had unleashed. And yet, every fibre of her being knew that it couldn't be left like this. She must go on.

'Y-you've...' She swallowed, and forced it out. 'You've told me it wasn't your idea.' She looked down at her own agitated body, its pink signals still broadcasting from the hilltops, its secret hollow still pulsing desire no less urgent for being out of sight. 'Are you also going to tell me you weren't even tempted?'

In the long pause that followed, she felt his anger controlled and mastered. The thunder and lightning were still there within him, but on the surface all was calm.

'That,' he admitted carefully, 'is something else.'

'Were you?' she persisted, dreading the answer yet knowing she must hear it. 'Were you tempted?'

'I'm a man, aren't I?' The blue eyes met hers with brutal candour. 'Of course I was tempted.'

'Oh, you...' She made a dash for the door, flicked his silk dressing-gown from its peg, dragged it round her, and belted it tight. 'So now we're hearing it.' She shook her hair back and faced him anew. 'If I hadn't turned up——'

'Your turning up changed nothing.' Padding across the room, he stopped at the chair with Rachel's shirt on it. 'I'd already tried to put her clothes back on her——'

'I bet you both liked that.'

'Did I look as if I liked it?'

He picked up her azure silk shirt and crushed it together, just as he had done last night with Claudette's green velvet. A shudder ran through Rachel at the sight of those strong hands punishing her own garment, but she wouldn't be put off.

'Why ask me? I wasn't there.'

'*Yes, you damn well were.*'

The rafter-shaking bellow hit Rachel at the same time as the shirt did. It was the noise as much as the soft impact of the silk which knocked her weakened knees from under her. She sank to the edge of the bed with the dressing-gown armoured round her, and raised her chin, undaunted.

'So you're going to try violence again, are you?'

'Stop drivelling about things you don't understand.' He still breathed fast, but the explosion seemed to have brought him some release. 'Your idea of violence is being sent to bed without your supper——'

'Whereas yours is pushing women about.'

Abruptly calm, he faced her. 'Do you really want so much to pick a fight with me?'

'Certainly not.' She managed a little laugh which she hoped was scornful. 'All I'm trying to do is sort things out.'

'So sort!' The steel-flashing eyes drilled into hers. 'Ask yourself what self-respecting man would have anything to do with that little...' he choked back an ugly word '...would stand the way she was coming on last night. Go on,' he urged as he saw her wavering. 'Think about it.'

Rachel wanted to refuse, but couldn't. She couldn't even shake her head. She bore his gaze for a moment more, hoping to stare him down, but it was no use—she never could outface him in a contest of wills like this. In the end she always had to submit, and turn her own eyes away, as she did now, to break the spell. Staring, unfocused, at the tree-dappled shadows over the blond floorboards, she found herself doing what he had bidden, thinking back over her fatigue-soaked memories of last night.

He followed up his advantage. 'You know where I'd got to when you knocked?'

'I . . . I don't want to . . .'

'Tough, because you're damn well going to.' He took the chair he had freed of her clothes, and straddled it with his arms resting on the back. 'I'd decided to put the little menace in my car, and get her back to her parents somehow.'

'What?' Rachel burst into a hysterical giggle at the thought of him driving a naked girl through the town and bundling her back where she came from.

'You can imagine how much good that would have done me with the Greniers.' He let the idea sink home. 'Do you still think I was enjoying myself?'

She turned to him, almost convinced. 'You really, truly weren't?'

'Would you? Supposing . . .' he paused, thinking up an example ' . . . supposing the husband of your best mate cornered you. Would you enjoy it?'

'Of course not, but——'

'Even if he was good-looking, and turned you on physically?'

'*Nobody* turns me on physically except . . .' she turned from that brilliant steel-blue gaze ' . . . except you.'

'Jelly-tot!' Gentle and loving, he was suddenly by her on the bed, that dear arm round her. 'Why are you doing this to us?'

'*I'm* not doing it.' She hunched away. 'You're the one who's...' she sifted back over what he had just told her '...who's admitted that Claudette Grenier turns you on.'

'Did I?' He considered it. 'Well, why not? These things happen.'

'They don't!' She stared up at him, horrified at this new gulf opening between them. 'Not when you're faithful. That's what it's all about——'

'Rubbish!' He made one of those powerful, sweeping gestures, brushing aside her illusions. 'Faithfulness doesn't mean never being tempted. It means not giving in when you are.'

'But Ned...' She swallowed hard. 'How...how many times have you been t-tempted, then, since we were together?'

'Who's counting?'

Hit by the new shock of finding his view so different from her own, she thought back over the years. Now she knew this about him, the incidents with other women showed in quite another light.

'So you really *wanted* to go to bed with that Carol North?'

'Her with the paint, and the eyelashes?' He could actually grin at the memory. 'In my single days I might have tried undoing all that pretty packaging, yes.'

'And that Elsa Davis?'

'The one who led her husband such a dance? What kind of an idiot do you take me for?' He grinned again. 'Now, that little Alice Norman—remember her?'

'Scoop necklines, bleached hair,' Rachel recalled in disgust. 'You can't have fancied *her*?'

'She'd a nice little chassis on her, that one.'

'There's no need to be so vulgar.'

'Look.' He brought her back to his theme. 'Since we've been together, I haven't made love to anybody but you.'

'You expect me to believe that now?'

'Yes, I damn well do. I believe it about you.'

'I haven't been caught with someone in my room. This room.' She glanced about its innocent angles and nooks. 'Just think. You undressed two women here in as many hours, and didn't score with either.'

'Why, you little...' His head snapped up in renewed rage. 'Now who's being vulgar?' he demanded, in control once more. 'Let's stick to the point, shall we? Do you really believe I'd...go astray...with Monsieur Grenier's daughter?'

Utterly confused, she let her head droop so that her hair swung forward and covered her eyes. Within its many-stranded veil, she looked again at the case he had just made out, and had to admit it held together.

But that only emphasised this other feeling—of having completely lost her bearings. For two years she'd been safely settled with a man she'd known all her life, and now he was telling her things which showed she'd never known him at all.

'Poor Jel.' His voice was suddenly much gentler. 'You should never have to be bothered with harpies like that little Claudette.'

'You call her a harpy, and...lots of other things...' Rachel shook her hair back, needing to see him '...and yet you wanted her?'

He smiled, the fond smile she thought of as being just for her. 'Did you want that bread and jam just now?'

'What's that got to do——?'

'She's a bit like that—sexual bread and jam. Only in her case, it's pretty poisonous——'

'Poisonous!' The ugly word at once conjured up a picture of that lurid-coloured letter. 'Ned, we've got to talk.'

'We certainly have.' He glared down at where his robe swelled over her breasts, narrowed to her waist, swelled again to her hips. 'There's this business of the Pill to thrash out.'

'There's also...' She broke off, stood up, and went to the handbag he had dumped in the corner with the rest of her luggage.

'Look.' She drew out the letter and handed it to him. 'You'd better read this while I'm showering.'

CHAPTER THREE

'I FEEL as if you've changed to a whole different person.'
Rachel wasn't aware of her sigh until it mingled with the
soft May wind. In the tangle of vines shading their bench,
the young leaves shivered. A tiny spider went spinning
away from its scouting place before their faces, its
gossamer tarzan rope glinting through the dappled light
and disappearing somewhere near the sun-warmed wall.

'I thought I'd known you all my life,' she went on,
'and now it turns out I've been living two years with a
stranger.'

'You and me both.' Ned stared sombrely over the hotel's gravelled garden with its central collection of potted
plants. 'I want a family as much as you do——'

'I know that,' she cut in, irritated that he should keep
harking back to this minor problem.

'So how come I get left out of the decision to start
one?'

'I didn't leave you out.'

'No? And when were you planning to discuss it?'

'Well . . . soon . . .'

'Like,' his lips compressed, 'when we're all set to roll
and roll.'

'Ned!'

But he only raised his voice to a smug, feminine falsetto. '"Yes, please, darling. But I'd better tell you—it
could make me pregnant."'

44

She clenched her fists, glaring at the hot-red Canna lilies rising stiff and fleshy from their terracotta pots. 'I didn't mean to do it like that.'

'So what had you in mind?' The lithe body flexed at her side, the glinting fair head turning to survey her. 'To get the baby going, and then tell me?'

'Certainly not!'

She jerked round to meet his gaze, colour flooding to her cheeks. The steel-blue eyes, cool and distant and scalpel-sharp, laid bare ideas within herself which she hadn't known she was harbouring.

'O-of course not,' she stammered with ever less conviction. 'I m-mean...' She trailed off, heel scuffing the gravel. 'Anyway,' her anger flared anew, 'I don't know how you had the nerve to...' she faltered at the memory of it '...to try and make love to me, after the way I found you out.'

'Now don't start that again. You found out nothing.'

'Claudette Grenier——'

'Could happen to anybody. Like a bluebottle in the kitchen.'

'Some bluebottle. And what about this letter?' She fished in her pocket, and set the ball of crumpled paper on the rustic table, shaking her head. 'Whatever came over you?'

'Sheer blind rage.' He blew at some invisible entanglement—perhaps the spider thread had drifted to his face. 'If I could have got my hands on the little madam...'

Rachel suppressed a helpless giggle. 'You'd hardly throw the lady herself out of the window after her letter?'

'It's just lucky she wasn't about.'

As it turned out, Rachel hadn't made it to the shower. He had accepted the offered letter, and read it while she went to her bag in search of clean clothes. The next thing she knew was another of those huge roars.

'The little...hag!'

She'd jumped round, to find Ned electric with fury. His whole formidable frame had shot to attention, his eyes lightning-blue, his uncombed hair wiry and gold-sparking, his raised fists clenched round the heavy rose-pink paper and its purple envelope. Under Rachel's fascinated eyes the strong hands had come together, crushing pink and purple into a single garish ball. Then the purposeful arm had risen in its dazzling white sleeve, and the ball sailed past her through the open window.

'For heaven's sake, Ned!'

She'd rushed to the window, pulling the dressing-gown round her, and stuck out her head. Below, the two-coloured ball of paper littered the gravel, bleached by the morning sunlight.

'You don't,' Rachel had snapped, 'need to spread our private life all over the hotel garden.'

'That...that *thing*——' he'd joined her at the window, breathing hard '—is nothing whatever to do with us.'

'It's addressed to me, it mentions you by name—who else would it be about?'

'I won't be held responsible for the fantasy life of every little mischief-maker...'

'I'd better get down there, before somebody comes along and reads it.'

Pulling on yesterday's clothes, Rachel had rushed down to the garden. By the time he joined her there, she had whisked up the offending letter and stuffed it in her pocket, in case he meant to punish it further.

But his quick anger had vanished at once in the hot sunlight. For a moment they'd faced each other, caught in a wafting web of perfumes from the sun-warmed blossoms and leaves. Then, without a word, they had made for the vine-shaded rustic bench where they now sat.

This was how it had always been between them. She'd always known instinctively what he wanted, and trusted him to know the same about her. Generally, the two things had been one.

Or so I believed, she thought, and listened to the fussing of birds among the Virginia creeper on the house wall.

'This is so different from an English garden,' she observed wistfully. 'Gravel instead of lawn, and all these gorgeous potted plants together in the middle.'

'Clever, isn't it?' he agreed, equally glad to rest a moment from their quarrel. 'D'you see the bay tree, and the azalea?'

'And lupins, irises, marigolds, snapdragons, alyssum...'

She gave up trying to identify the endless flowers. Each flourished in its own pot, each pot set into the little mound of gravel which rose to a wistaria-hung stone plinth. On the plinth, a stone vase held a rosebush like a bride's bouquet, riotous with coral-pink buds.

'It really makes me feel...' Rachel paused, to give the fine word its due importance '...makes me feel *abroad*, this garden does. If only...'

Another sigh escaped her as her glance fell once more to the table. She had put the wretched letter there, still crumpled together with its grape-purple, rose-pink-lined envelope. It might be in a sorry state now, but its message must be dealt with. She smoothed the paper and read once more the huge script.

Mademoiselle,

This is about Mr Flavell. You are very bad for him and it is wrong of you to hold him when he should be free. It is bad enough that he is tied to a woman at all, a man of his temperament, but a woman such as you, who knows nothing of art, it is impossible. Please, *mademoiselle*, set him free to become the great sculptor he should be. If you do not, I think you may lose him in any case.

Cordially yours,
A Friend.

'Give it here,' he growled, reaching for it. 'Let's find somewhere we can burn it.'

Rachel refused to surrender it. 'You're sure it's from Claudette?'

'Who else would write such rubbish?'

'And...it is rubbish?' she faltered, clinging to the letter. 'You really don't want to...I don't know...live in a garret in Paris, and produce great works of art?'

He had always spoken so lightly of his pleasure in shaping odd bits of wood. Now, though, she wondered if it was more important to him than he would admit. Some of his carvings at home were infinitely satisfying—the woodland scene from left-over pine planking, for instance, and the fox from a tree root.

'Great works of art, indeed.' He captured the letter from her reluctant fingers, and waved it in disgust. 'I half whittle an otter, and suddenly I'm Giambologna.'

'Who?' she asked, lost for a moment.

'Italian guy.' His irritation softened to the old, teasing smile. 'Don't worry, he isn't hot news.'

She drooped in depression. 'You needn't condescend to me, just because I don't know about art.'

'And you think Claudette Grenier does?' Another snort. 'Not if it dropped dead in front of her.'

'Still...' Rachel struggled with her new worries. 'You've started on an otter, you said?'

He nodded. 'I found a piece of applewood in the Greniers' winter fuel, just the right shape.'

'Which you'd spot at once.' She recalled his treasure store of such pieces, waiting to be finished to the shape he saw in them. 'Maybe she's right. Maybe you should——'

'Dammit, this is poison pen stuff!' He tore the letter across, and across again. 'You shouldn't even be taking it seriously, let alone rushing here at a moment's notice...' He paused in his paper shredding. 'How did you manage to get the time off work so quickly?'

'By not rushing at a moment's notice,' she retorted. 'I'd already applied for a few days' leave, to come here and surprise you.' The irony of it surged over her. 'Which I certainly did.'

'Not again!' His eagle profile tilted a little, calling heaven to witness his patience. 'How the hell can we thrash out the serious stuff, when you keep dragging that in?'

'Great.' She edged as far away from him as the arm of the bench would let her. 'If it's something *you* want to talk about, that's serious. If it's only me who's interested—— '

'Will you for heaven's sake get your head together?' He thumped the table, fist still clenched round the pink and purple scraps. 'What could be more important than our having a family, and changing our whole life together?'

She turned to face him, prepared at last to argue her case. 'For a start, it might never happen.'

'Which would also be serious. Or are you telling me——' the steel-blue eyes took hers again, clear-sighted and uncompromising '—that it doesn't matter if it turns out we can't have children?'

'Don't say things like that!' She shut her own eyes, and covered her ears with her hands to keep out the dreaded thought. 'You've no business putting that into my mind, just to——'

'See?' He leaned back, triumphant. 'Now will you admit this matters, and stop dragging in nonsense like my bad luck with the Grenier girl?'

Shut off from the springing world by her closed eyes, her closed ears, for a moment she wouldn't move. Then his cruel logic filtered through all her guards, and she knew she had to submit.

'All right.' Slowly, reluctantly, she took her hands from her ears, and opened her eyes. 'What do you want to say about it?'

He made a soft movement, perhaps to brush away a spider-web, perhaps to free himself from that dizzying web of spring perfumes. 'You left off your Pill without a word to me.'

Aware that he meant her to answer, and wouldn't let go until she did, she bowed her head in agreement.

'And you'd never have told me about it, would you,' he went on, 'if you hadn't been annoyed with me?'

She pushed away the memory of their frustrating, unfinished lovemaking. 'I like "annoyed". As if I'd caught you squeezing the wrong end of the toothpaste tube.'

'How many times do I have to say it, woman?' He sighed, ready to say it again. 'If you'd never existed, you still wouldn't catch me squeezing Claudette Grenier, any end.'

'Silly.' It was the old, loving word they used for each other's absurdities, but she couldn't muster the slightest smile to go with it.

Nor was there any answering smile in the steel-blue eyes which burnt so urgently into hers. 'If I can't convince you of that, you don't know anything at all about me.'

'Which is exactly where we came in,' she admitted, depressed.

A dark and pale bird darted over the rough-timbered roof of the outbuilding ten yards away. Rachel watched it drop and cling, and shaded her eyes to make out its mud nest, a miniature cave in the shade of the eaves.

'House-martins,' Ned told her with none of his usual interest. 'This seat's perfect for watching them.'

She recalled her own special reason for liking these particular birds. 'Aren't they one of the kind where the cock does his share of the work all the way through?'

He nodded. 'Helps build the nest, sits on the eggs, feeds the young...'

'The perfect father, in fact.'

'But, then,' Ned pointed out, 'he only has to do it for part of the year. The rest of it, he travels.'

'Is that what you really want to do then? Travel again?'

She couldn't keep the dismay out of her voice. In his late teens, while most of his friends were in college or starting work, Ned had taken off with a backpack. He returned four years later, deeply tanned, still only twenty-two, but to her eyes infinitely more mature and interesting than men ten years his senior. He had at once set up the first Flavell's, and in the nine years since had shown no signs of wanting to take off again.

'I thought nowadays,' she prompted him, 'our holidays were enough for you.'

'They are. Of that kind of travel.'

She was speechless for a moment, stunned by the slight contempt in his tone. Was this really how he thought of the expensive holidays she had enjoyed so much?

'We certainly are finding things out,' she murmured at last.

'And needed to know them,' he agreed. 'I suppose I should be grateful to blasted young Claudette.'

'Grateful?' she echoed, astonished again at his nerve.

'I gather,' he went on doggedly, 'that you were coming here anyway, letter or no letter?'

'Yes, but——'

'So if Claudette hadn't got in our way, I'd have taken you straight to bed for an old-fashioned welcome.'

'Oh!' She flung her head back, trying to shake off the longing his terse words had roused in her. 'You're so damn sure of yourself!'

'The sort of welcome——' his voice hardened, forcing her to listen '——that makes babies.'

'There's no way of knowing——'

'Will you face the facts, woman?'

She glared up into the relentless, steel-blue gaze. 'You talk as if I were pregnant already.'

'Exactly,' he shot back in triumph. 'You could be, and me none the wiser. The first I'd know of it,' he added into her helpless silence, 'would have been my son or daughter on the way.'

Once more she had to admit the truth of his words. She was suddenly aware that until now her perception of the hoped-for baby had been of a cuddly bundle to hold and gurgle at and care for. Hearing Ned speak of his future son or daughter somehow altered the whole picture.

She tried again, puzzled by her need to defend her decision. 'It's a woman's business, deciding about a family.'

He sat bolt upright. 'You've been talking to my mother.'

'As if I would!'

'Listening to her, then.' He went falsetto again, deeper this time. '"Men always think they can wait." That's one of hers.'

Rachel blinked. His insulting attempt at her own voice had been nonsense—hadn't it? Listening to him doing his mother's comfortable drawl, she wasn't so sure.

'And she's always saying, "Every baby brings its own love with it."' His closely observed voice portrait caught his mother's husky undertone exactly. 'You may not have openly agreed with her. You may have said, "All in good time…"'

'I don't talk like that,' Rachel interrupted, newly appalled at the self-satisfied note he had given his mimicry of her.

Could this be another of his talents that she'd neglected? She'd never heard him imitate any voice before, but he'd certainly got his mother right. Could it be that his version of herself was more accurate than she cared to admit? Did she really sound so bossy and complacent?

But this was ridiculous—why was she letting him undermine all her ideas about herself? If he insisted on questioning her decision to try for a baby, she could at least state her case.

'I'm twenty-six, you're thirty-one,' she reminded him. 'We can't hang about forever.'

'Sure. And if you'd talked to me, I might have agreed.'

'There you are, then.'

'But you weren't going to. Not until...' He paused, then brought out the cruel bluntness in his mind. 'Not until I was trapped.'

She tensed in shock. 'What a rotten thing to say.'

'It's a rotten way to feel.'

'But...you like living with me, don't you?'

'It's not so bad. Considering it was entirely your idea.'

'Ned!' She stared at him, stricken.

'Well, perhaps not only yours,' he admitted, softening. 'Cheer up.'

Suddenly gentle, he reached out, and before she knew it his fingers were cool at the nape of her neck. She moved angrily to shake them off, leaning over the arm of the bench as far from him as possible.

It wasn't far enough. His hand stayed with her, smoothing through the thickness of her hair, sliding under her shirt collar to massage the tension from the top of her spine.

And, for all her resistance, languor and excitement rayed over her from his touch. She closed her eyes tight and shook her head, refusing to give in to it, but that was worse. To her enraged surprise, she found tears smarting under her closed lids.

She forced them back. 'I didn't exactly have to hold you down while I kissed you.'

'Oh, kissing——'

'Doesn't mean a thing?'

'Not what I was going to say.'

'So what *were* you going to say?'

He shrugged. 'I don't know. It doesn't matter.'

'But it does,' she insisted. 'You can't start a show-down and then just walk away from it.'

'A show-down.' The loved, deep-seeing eyes turned to her. 'Is that what you think I've begun?'

'Well, haven't you? I never knew you even had words like...' she gulped '...like "trapped" in your mind. Or that our living together was all my idea.'

'I was only saying——'

'That you're not as contented as I thought you were.'

'Could be.' He considered the idea. 'As it happens, I do think we're just a bit too settled.'

'What's wrong with settled?'

'It can make you complacent.'

That word again. It echoed in her mind, dragging her back to the startling ideas his imitation of her voice had roused in her.

'There I'd be,' he went on, 'out of the race before I'd——'

'You can hardly say before you'd played the field,' she cut in, 'considering the number of girlfriends you've had.'

He clicked his tongue impatiently. 'Let me finish.'

'Sorry.' But try as she would, she couldn't sound sorry. 'What were you trying to say, then?'

'That I don't feel I've done anything yet.'

'But that's ridiculous. Now if it had been me you were talking about...' She broke off, comparing her own safe routine at the Water Board with his enterprise and daring. 'You started Flavell's from nothing...'

'Nine years ago.' And he actually sighed, as if for happy times gone by.

'You surely can't have enjoyed all that?' Rachel felt her mouth drop open in astonishment. 'All those weeks covered in plaster-dust and glue and wood-shavings...'

'Fitting out my own premises, exactly as I wanted them.'

She nodded, forced to see what he meant. Ned was essentially practical, relishing rough jobs and never happier than when he could work with his hands. But surely he could see how much better off he was now?

'All right, you enjoyed setting up that first restaurant. But what about those early days?' She tried again to remind him of the tough reality behind his rosy memories. 'You as a one-man band? Cooking, waiting on tables, clearing up...'

'Organising supplies, balancing books, thinking up ways to get the public in.' He smiled, seeing a completely different picture from the one she was trying to present. 'It was great.'

'But you surely wouldn't want to be back again with nothing?'

'And all to play for? I don't know.' He stared at the bustling house-martins, not seeing them. 'I sometimes think it rots you, being too comfortable.'

'But...' She choked, and tried again. 'You're always so careful about comfort! When you're starting a new restaurant...'

She floundered to a halt. How many times had she listened while he lovingly described airy kitchens, quiet dining-rooms big enough to take the generous tables he insisted on, luxurious cloakrooms which made an experience out of powdering your nose? He wouldn't buy any premises that didn't have the potential to make his diners feel like royalty, yet here he was speaking of comfort as if it were an enemy.

'It's high time I moved on to something else,' he announced, as if he had just now fully realised it.

'Wh-what else?' she ventured, small and quavery. 'What else had you in mind?'

She looked down in her lap and found her hands clenched tight. She really needed the answer to this one. Did he want to give up his controlling interest in the

Flavell empire, and leave Caster, and start something new? Because if so, if that was what he needed to use up his endless energy, then she must back him.

But supposing his ideas didn't include her at all? Supposing he wanted to leave her, too? The ugly word "trapped" rang again in her head, and her fingers interlocked.

'H-hotels?' She hardly recognised her own timid croak. 'You could make Flavell's an international name for quality...'

His vigorous headshake put an end to that idea. 'It would only be more of the same. In fancy dress.'

Anxious though she was, she had to smile. He did so hate formality of any kind. He even dodged wearing a tie unless she made him.

Then her worries came back in full force. "More of the same". Did he really see his life as a mere dismal routine? And if he did, were her plans for a family merely another part of the same well-known, tedious pattern?

'So really,' she began slowly, trying to recognise and accept the painful fact, 'you're bored with...life in general?'

He nodded. 'Have been for months.'

'And...' She swallowed again, then tackled it head-on. 'And with me?'

She thought she would wait forever for the answer. The strongly marked eyebrows drew together, sha-dowing the steel-blue eyes while they stared out at nothing.

'Not of loving you.' And yet he didn't move to touch or even glance at her. 'That's the plus side of the deal.'

'Is that how you think of our life together?' She looked away from him, out to where the blaze of flowers and the green and gold of leaves had all paled to miserable gray. 'A deal?'

He turned to survey her. Aware of him as ever, she felt the gentleness of the movement. Though she refused to look up, she knew that the gold-maned head would be tilted towards her, the square-tipped hand moving to take hers. She edged further from him, and spread her own hand to ward him off.

'Don't. Now we're in it, we'd better keep going.' She mustered all her strength. 'A deal, you said.'

'It's only a way of putting it.' The wide shoulder next to her lifted and dropped, shrugging off the significance. 'I'm a dealer, love, for better or for worse——'

'And don't call me love,' she snapped. 'Not now.'

It wasn't what she'd meant to say. But, then, she hardly knew what she had meant, except to ward off her pain at that casual phrase, 'for better or for worse'.

She'd always known she'd take Ned Flavell for better or for worse, for richer or for poorer, in sickness and in health. Yes, and she'd love and honour him, if ever he asked her.

If only he'd ask her.

Looking back, she seemed to have been in love with him all her life. Her family told her that as soon as she could toddle she had staggered after him, determined to be included in his mysterious, important, six-year-old world. Her own memories only went back to her first schooldays, when ten-year-old Ned had taken over her brother's job of meeting her at the gate and seeing her safely home. And when she changed schools at eleven there was Ned, a lordly sixth-former, willing to take time off his urgent A level studies to chat with her in front of the whole playground.

After that, he'd simply gone beyond her reach. First he'd disappeared abroad, and then, when she was settled in her job and he returned from his wanderings, he'd hardly noticed her. He'd been deeply involved with the first restaurant, and then with all the others he was setting up in different parts of the country. In his scant leisure, he amused himself with a seemingly endless string of girls, each prettier than the last, none staying.

'It's now or never,' she'd told herself on her twenty-second birthday.

That was when she had set out to make him see her as a woman, rather than merely as a part of his childhood. Even now, she wasn't quite sure how she'd brought it off. Determination, single-mindedness, attention to detail? Sheer refusal to give up a pursuit which so often seemed hopeless?

She'd planned every step. She'd learnt where he bargained for fresh vegetables, and just happened to be visiting that farm herself, perfectly turned out in country casuals, on the day he went there. She'd read all she could about vintage cars, and spent afternoons at auctions for the sake of the brief wave he might give her while he chatted to fellow enthusiasts. She'd got herself invited to any party given by any friend they had in common, though mostly he didn't turn up or, if he did, left early with some other girl while Rachel fended off some other man.

That was how things stood when, at last, she'd met him by real chance after all. Walking the family dog in the woods, thinking of nothing but her enjoyment of the soft summer rain, she'd felt her heart turn over at the sight of the familiar tall figure ahead.

Of all times for this to happen! She was miserably conscious of her swathing headscarf, unpainted face, clumsy rubber boots, and of the old anorak which had once been blue but had long since faded to the colour of the rain itself, a watery grey.

'Mick!' she'd hissed to the dog, hoping to dodge out of sight before it was too late.

But already Mick was pattering away from her, tongue lolling in cheerful greeting. Rachel had to follow.

And Ned, dear Ned, hadn't even noticed her general drabness. Alive with excitement, he'd parted the leaves at the edge of the path to show her the creatures clinging beneath.

'D'you know what these are?'

'Slugs?' Rachel choked back her disgust by sheer effort of will. 'I suppose the rain——'

'Caterpillars,' he'd corrected her, 'of the Purple Hairstreak Butterfly.' He uttered the strange name in a huge whisper, as if these crawling green grubs might suddenly take fright and vanish. 'Hardly ever seen in this country. Hell, if only I weren't heading for Nottingham...'

She learnt that he wanted some of the plants potted and kept safe, caterpillars and all. Caterpillars *especially*, to see them through the chrysalis stage until they hatched out as butterflies.

'But I haven't even a trowel with me,' he'd fretted. 'And the birds or the shrews are bound to get them before I'm back.'

That was when Rachel had made the great offer which changed her life. Knowing how busy he was, how little time he could spare for things like taking care of caterpillars, she took a deep breath and hardened herself against nausea to come.

'Can I do it?'

And so she'd won Ned Flavell. He'd departed for Nottingham; she had returned to the woods with a spade and an old fruit box, wincing as she handled the infested plants and hoped the slug-like creatures would stay where they belonged, rather than crawl over her car.

'Just think of them as babies,' she'd told herself as she tended them in the one-room flat she'd insisted on moving into when she started her job. 'Helpless little things that need you.'

To her surprise, it worked. In the five days Ned was away she'd grown quite fond of her little green babies. When he rang her on his return and offered to take them over, she'd refused to give them up.

'I'm not having them disturbed again. You can visit them here, if you like.'

And he did.

Months later, when they moved into their chosen flat, one iridescent purple butterfly went with them in a glass frame. Not that they'd killed the butterfly babies, of course. They'd found this one in the woods, peacefully dead of old age after a long and fruitful life, or so she hoped.

Ned still sometimes teased her by referring to the caterpillars that had first brought them together. She never contradicted him. He didn't need to know how very much earlier it had all really started for her.

She'd kept that idea to herself, and yet now it came as a shock to learn how he, too, had ideas he'd kept to himself. A deal, he'd called their love—*her* love—a deal with a plus side and a minus.

'So what,' she persisted, 'is the minus side?'

Another shrug. 'I thought I'd said it. Always having another person to consider before I do anything.'

'But Ned, I try so hard not to get in your way.' She offered an example. 'I didn't stop you making this trip, did I?'

An ironic gleam lit the steel-blue eyes. 'You really think that proves something?'

'Well, doesn't it? I know you need to be alone now and then, so I let you travel without me.'

'And went right ahead with your own plans. One——' he raised a finger to count it off '—to join me here. Two—just by the way, of course—to start a family.'

Had she really been so over-confident? she wondered, and shivered in the suddenly cold sunlight. 'I did give you a week on your own. And look what you did with it,' she added in renewed indignation.

'Not Claudette again, please. Look——' he consulted his watch '—I'm due at the Greniers' for lunch in fifteen minutes—— '

'What?' She turned to stare at him in dismay. 'You're going to see her again, after all you've said?'

'I'm lunching with the entire Grenier family. All four of them,' he corrected her, and swung to his feet in one businesslike movement. 'The deal isn't clinched yet.'

'Another deal.' She stared gloomily up to his great height, blinking against the dazzle of sunlight on his shirt and hair.

'Cheer up, love.' He offered his hand to draw her up to him. 'The time'll soon pass.'

'As if you cared!'

She rose energetically, thrusting his hand aside. His only reaction was to turn away, ignoring her dramatics to savour the scents of good cooking from the kitchen.

'That smells good. I almost wish I were having it with you.'

She drooped once more. 'I'm not a bit hungry.'

'Rubbish,' he contradicted her sharply. 'After starving yourself all yesterday, of course you're hungry.'

'I'd eat like anything——' she glanced up sideways through her lashes '—if you'd only stay here with me.'

'Don't put it on me, Jel. Eat for yourself, because you need to.'

She nodded, and silently contemplated the dismal prospect.

'Madame Grenier will have been cooking all morning,' he added on a gentler note. 'You've heard of a woman scorned?' He did an exaggerated shudder. 'Picture a Frenchwoman with a scorned *brochet meunière* on her hands.'

'She could always,' Rachel suggested rebelliously, 'freeze it for later.'

'They'd think that a barbaric suggestion. If Monsieur Grenier even suspected I run a freezer——' Ned glanced at his watch, and steered them towards the hotel's back entrance '—he'd probably refuse to sell me his wine.'

Resigned, she let herself be steered. 'You honestly think he'd call the deal off over a stupid thing like that?'

'I don't know. But he certainly would if I cried off lunch at this stage.' Ned opened the door, and stood back to let her through. 'He's an old-fashioned Frenchman, Monsieur Grenier. He takes his food seriously.'

She swallowed a yawn. 'You'll come back quickly?'

'Can't promise, love. French meals are never quick.'

'And all that time,' she realised in depression, 'you'll be with Claudette Grenier.'

'*And* her family,' he pointed out.

'I still don't like it.'

'I promised, love.' It wasn't a plea, but rather a closing of the argument.

Rachel sighed. How like him to insist on holding to a promise made, and refusing to make one he couldn't keep. But, then, wasn't that why she loved him?

CHAPTER FOUR

'TEN miles?' Rachel tilted the telephone receiver in resentful surprise. 'To taste a *cheese*?'

'A very special cheese——' Ned's voice on the line held the merest hint of mockery '—only made on this one farm.'

'Are you hoping to buy some?'

'Could do. That's why Monsieur Grenier's going. Apparently this is the best time of year for it.'

'How,' she asked, puzzled as ever at the vagaries of the food trade, 'does the time of year affect the taste of cheese?'

'The pastures are at their richest in May,' he explained. 'Therefore, so is the milk. Therefore, the cheese——'

'All right, all right.' She didn't want to know that much about cheese. 'How will you ever get enough from just one farm?'

'I wouldn't be buying for the restaurants, silly.' He really did laugh now, indulgently. 'Only a little, for ourselves. I'm calling to tell you why I won't be back this afternoon.'

'Not the whole afternoon?' she wailed in growing dismay. 'And what am *I* supposed to do?'

'It's surely not beyond you to do a bit of exploring on your own?' he suggested, totally unsympathetic. 'I did, before you arrived.'

'While you go on a lovely run into the hills.' She pictured him in the two-seater, bright hair blowing. 'I suppose in weather like this you'll have the top folded down?'

'I'm here with the Saab, not the Alfa Romeo,' he reminded her. 'Anyway, we're taking Monsieur Grenier's Citroën.' Ned's voice dropped confidentially. 'He says he needs the space...'

'Space?' She stiffened. 'Who else is going, then?'

'Only *madame*. Claudette's taking her own car, being newly acquainted with it...'

'She will be with you, though? You're leaving me alone down here——' Rachel seethed at the idea '—while you jaunt off with Claudette Grenier?'

A pause on the other end of the line, and then his voice came out clipped and abrupt. 'Leave it, Jel.'

'I just hope that you... that you all fall in the cheese vat,' she hissed into the receiver. '*And don't call me Jel*!'

She whipped the telephone from her ear to slam into its wall holster. Before she could get it there, it roared back at her, 'And don't you dare hang up on me!'

Even reduced by distance, the noise frightened her. She let the instrument tremble an inch from its cradle, then reluctantly returned it to her ear. He must have lowered his own receiver—she could hear him some way off, murmuring in French. So he was using the Grenier phone, and would now be apologizing for shouting. If he was with Monsieur Grenier only, he'd be adding something rude about women.

She had a little more privacy here. The phone in the bar of the Hotel du Centre had no booth of its own, but at least it was well down the cloakroom corridor, and the bar itself dozed in the mid-afternoon lull. Only Monsieur Durand, on the same high stool as last night, whiled away the hottest part of the day with murmured chat to Madame Robert. Neither showed any sign of having heard Ned's outburst.

'Bullying won't help,' Rachel snapped, partly in defiance and partly in craven submission, to show she was still there.

Ned's voice came back in brusque English. 'And don't try the schoolma'am stuff, either.'

'You had something more to say?' She clenched the receiver to control her fury. 'Seeing you've kept me here?'

'My host's daughter——' the roundabout phrasing would be to make sure Monsieur Grenier didn't understand '—will not be in the car with us. She might turn up at the farm, but that's not very——'

'If she even *might*,' Rachel interrupted, 'then I'm surprised you're going.'

What really surprised her, if she were honest with herself, was her own vehemence. Generally she didn't dare to so much as answer Ned back when he was in this mood, let alone scold him.

Maybe it was Madame Robert's superb *coq au vin* which had given her the courage. She'd certainly eaten enough of it.

When she'd finished it, she'd felt gloriously idle. Content just to be alive, she'd drifted outdoors, through scents of roses and honeysuckle, to the wooden bench under the vines. Once there, soothed by the humming, twittering warmth, she'd decided that she could really do a lot worse than wait, in this essence-of-abroad garden, for the great moment of Ned's return. Presently the leaf-green, sky-blue, flower-spangled scene had disappeared under the sunny pink haze of her closed eyelids. When she was a little girl, she'd always pretended at bedtime to be the sleeping princess, waiting for the prince to wake her with a kiss...

What did wake her, an uncountable time later, was the firm, professionally respectful voice of Madame Robert. 'Telephone, *mademoiselle*. It is Monsieur Ned, I think.'

And here he was, with this outrageous news, and an even more outrageous anger with her for objecting to it.

'Have you ever thought, Jel——' his steely tones, though reduced by the earpiece, still forced her attention '—of letting me finish a sentence? Just now and then?'

'Tasting cheese, for heaven's sake.'

'That's very much how Clau...' he stopped, and discreetly corrected himself '...how the young lady here sees it,' he went on, smooth as if he hadn't made the mistake. 'Which is one reason why she's unlikely to go all the way up there with us.'

'What's the other reason? That she's only interested if she can be alone with you?'

'That her father——' he gave a rebuking weight to the word '—doesn't think she's experienced enough yet.'

'The way she's going, she'll soon be as experienced as a—— '

'*Jel*!'

'And don't call me Jel!'

Maybe she wasn't as safe from being overheard as she believed. Monsieur Durand had turned on his high stool, his broad, weatherbeaten face creased in amused curiosity. Behind him at the bar, less amused, Madame Robert shrugged. Rachel flashed an apologetic glance, uncomfortably aware of how much *madame* had already heard of these arguments between herself and Ned.

'The road——' his voice came hissing down the line, each word clipped off with hot precision '—is narrow, steep and winding. Too difficult for an inexperienced driver.'

'If she's that shaky——' Rachel rapped out the question between lips still stretched into a false half-smile for Madame '—why is she taking her car at all?'

'Because her father didn't like the idea. She's just flaming contrary, like all the rest of you women.'

'Are you putting me in the same category as that little—— ?'

'She's trying to prove she could get there if she wanted to.' He dragged them back to the business in hand. 'But no way is she ever going to make it as far as the Tour des Chats.'

'The what? That means tower of the cats,' Rachel translated. 'Doesn't sound like a farm to me.'

'Sorry about that,' he ground out in mock apology. 'Shall I get them to change the name for you?'

'There's no need to be sarcastic.'

'No need at all,' he agreed promptly. 'And no need for me to have spoken to you, either. It's turning out a complete waste of time.'

'You mean——' she kept her half-smile in place, and cooed furiously down the line '—you'd have just let me wait here, and worry, and not told me anything?'

'I could have left a message with Madame Robert,' he growled. 'I presume you wouldn't have carried on like this with her?'

'Of course not; *she* isn't the one who's...' Rachel trailed off, knowing how useless it was to repeat her grievance. 'So when do I finally get to see you?'

'Hang on, I'll ask.' He was back a moment later. 'About six, they think.'

'*Six*!' she repeated incredulously. 'You're staying with them the whole afternoon?'

'Did you seriously believe I wouldn't?'

'But...but...' She sought for words. 'You won't be buying this wretched cheese for the restaurants?'

'That's what I said.'

'So this is nothing but a...a pleasure-trip,' she choked. 'You're going on a pleasure-trip with another woman, on my first day in France.'

'*What* other woman—Madame Grenier? And I'd better remind you, Jel,' he added with deadly calm, 'that it was your idea for you to join me here, not mine. I've got work to do.'

'But you're not *doing* the work,' she wailed, her possible audience in the bar forgotten. 'You'll just be *enjoying* yourself—you said!'

'That's a matter of opinion...'

'I've a good mind to go straight back home.'

'Do. Then maybe I'll get to finish this job in peace.'

'I'll move out of our flat,' she stormed. 'I'll...I'll never speak to you again, Ned Flavell.'

'Haven't you learnt yet, Rachel Barclay——' the wretched man even sounded faintly bored '—never to make threats you can't carry out?'

'Oh!' She struggled for words. 'You're so damned...sure of yourself!'

'Compared to you, a new-hatched chick's sure of itself,' he told her with brisk affection. 'Why don't you grow up, Jel?'

'But Ned,' she pleaded, her anger fizzling out, 'you wouldn't leave me alone for as long as that?'

'I'll be back as soon as I comfortably can.' Clearly, for him the discussion was at an end. 'Now if you don't mind, I'll just get on with the job I came for.'

'Fetching cheese that there isn't enough of?'

'My host here can sell his...his *product* wherever he likes,' Ned reminded her. 'I intend that he sells it to *me*.'

She bit her lip, understanding at last. Ned never cared how much trouble he took to keep his quality up and his prices down. He meant to make friends with the man who could guarantee him steady supplies of a good, little-known wine and, if that included going on a cheese hunt, then on a cheese hunt he would go.

Rachel was prouder of the Flavell chain of restaurants than Ned was himself. Awed by all the testing and tasting and bulk buying, the transporting and handling and storing which made them such a success, she never knowingly got in their way. She mustn't this time, either.

Especially, she realised bitterly, since he was quite right about not having expected her to join him here. Cruel though it was of him to remind her, there was no reason why he should drop any engagement to be with her, let alone one so vital to him.

'I'm sure you'll get your wine,' she admitted, beaten.

'I will.'

'Yes. Good luck, Ned.'

'I don't need it, Jelly-tot. It'd be nice, though——' the warmth returned to his voice '—to see you smile when I get back.'

She tried, though it felt more like a wince of pain. Never mind, she had all afternoon to practice it.

'When you get back,' she promised, 'I'll smile.'

'Good girl. I'll bring you some cheese.'

'You needn't...'

She broke off. If he really made her a present of the wretched cheese, she'd take it away somewhere and jump on it. She'd kick it round the garden, and then flush it down the loo.

Curse Monsieur Grenier, she wanted to shout. Curse him and his wine and his daughter, and I hope they all choke on his mouldy ten-mile cheese.

Instead she drew a deep breath, composed her voice, and sent her most dulcet tone into the receiver. 'That'll be nice.'

'Till six, then.'

And that was it. There went this precious afternoon, lonely and lost without him as her lunchtime had been.

Still, her lunchtime hadn't been entirely lost, she reminded herself a little more cheerfully. She'd eaten a great meal, hadn't she? And there were adventures to be had, even alone. Maybe especially alone. For instance, without Ned to help with the language, merely chatting in the bar was an adventure. Passing through, she paused to thank Monsieur Durand for his last night's gift of brandy. When he understood, he wanted to buy her another, and Madame Robert had to rescue her by persuading him that coffee would be more suitable. Rachel drank it perched on the stool next to him, asking polite questions about the local crops and not understanding the answers.

But the coffee was good, rich and hot and fragrant. By the time she had finished it, she knew exactly what she was going to do. She would spend the afternoon exploring St-Jean-les-Chats on her own, and be able to talk to Ned about it when he came back with his wretched cheese. She smiled her thanks to Monsieur Durand, wished him and Madame Robert *au revoir*, and walked purposefully out into the cobbled street.

The heat outdoors reminded her why she'd changed into this loose cotton dress. Bare-legged and sandalled, she still had to saunter, and keep to the rare patches of shade on her walk up to the church. It proved to be locked, but she could admire the cat gargoyles, and the worn carving over the door. This must surely be of St Jean himself, a robed and bearded figure brandishing his stick at a flurry of retreating cat shapes.

'So what did you have against cats?' she asked him in the afternoon stillness. 'And once you'd chased them all away, how did you keep down the mice?'

St Jean kept his secrets, and so did the rest of the town. From here she could see how it was bounded on one side by the neat corduroy of what must be the Grenier vineyards, on the other by forested hills which stretched on and up to the horizon. Knowing exactly where Ned would have chosen to go had he been with her, she made straight for the forest.

Two hours later she was still walking up the steep pathway in the rustling, sun-flecked shade. A hare had lolloped away in front of her, and a tiny bank-vole, eating hungrily, had ignored her. She stored up questions for Ned about the woodpeckers whose rattling she could hear, and about why there were so very many tortoise-shell butterflies.

'The devil's butterfly,' Ned had once called those, and shrugged when she asked him why. 'I think the idea used to be that they were controlled by witches.'

At the time, it had seemed a mere intriguing fancy. Alone now in the green depths of the woods, Rachel found herself shivering as a pair of tortoiseshell wings brushed her cheek.

Presently, however, she found a stream lively with tiny brown fish. It led her down towards another side of town from the way she had come up, and at last fed through to—joy, oh, joy—a disused water-mill.

Here was something really special to ask Ned about. The bats roosting in the broken ceilings—he'd know the species—were a mere side attraction compared to this great moss-choked water-wheel, and the rusty machinery above it.

'A lot of huge iron wheels with teeth,' she memorised aloud so she could discuss it with him. 'Chains, hooks, weights...'

Still memorising, she continued her journey down to the edges of the town. She was so absorbed in her task that she almost walked on by the smart white house with the big gardens. To her it was just the place where the vineyards began, until she realised with a pang that it must be the Grenier residence.

And there's the Saab in the drive, she thought. It's waiting as I am, for Ned to finish the cheese hunt.

She glanced at her watch, and was astonished to find that it was already almost six. If she didn't go they might easily drive up and find her loitering here like a waif, far more pathetic than she felt after her lovely afternoon...

Yet she couldn't move on without searching the drive for the fabled orange car. She couldn't see it. Either it was inside one of those white garages, or—her heart sank—or Claudette really had joined the expedition, and had spent a happy afternoon with Ned, eating cheese... But that was so absurd that she had to giggle.

'Silly,' she told herself aloud in Ned's voice. 'You're getting paranoid.'

She hurried on, but stopped to watch a game of boule in the little tree-bordered public square. She had plenty of time; Ned couldn't return to the hotel without driving past her. If only he would, she reflected wistfully as she lingered by an old drinking trough, and again as she snuffed up the flowery, spicy scents of a private garden.

But he didn't, though when she reached the hotel the mirror-clock in the bar was registering quarter-past six.

Still, I've proved I can have a great time without you, she told Ned inside her head as she climbed the stairs to their room. I hardly thought about you at all, and anyway—her heart lifted as she hurried upwards—you'll be here in a minute.

Only he wasn't. She showered, dried her hair to a shining fall round her shoulders, and painted her nails. Still he didn't come, so she painted her toenails. Still no Ned: not when all the paint was dry, not when she had done a perfect make-up, not when she had mended the loose press-stud on her formal slip of a dress, not when she had put on the dress. Not when it was seven-thirty.

'He might at least have rung me,' she fretted aloud, and swayed down to the bar on her party heels.

A wall of masculine interest greeted her before ever she stepped off the stairs. She retreated hastily and, back in the room wondered what to do next. Should she brave all those staring Frenchmen, and try to ring the Grenier house? If she could get the right coins, and if—even less likely—she could master the French pay phone system.

And then I'd have to talk telephone French, she realised in dismay, with no sign language to help. Unless I happen to get Claudette, which would be worse.

Or would it? By half-past eight, she didn't care. She certainly couldn't go on like this, walking the floor and staring out of the windows and listening for cars pulling up outside.

'How can he do this to me?' she asked her smoothly groomed reflection. 'When I see him, I'll...'

But words failed her—she needed actions. Before she knew it, her party dress was flung away in favour of T-shirt, jeans, and a scarf to catch her hair to the back of her neck. She washed off her beautiful make-up almost with relief, and was ready, scrubbed and businesslike, to brave the bar again, as she must, to reach the street door.

Steady in her trainers, she walked once more down the stairs. As she had hoped, she attracted far less attention dressed like this. A single comment began as she entered the bar, but Madame Robert stemmed it with a glare.

'I'm—er—going for a little walk,' Rachel said quickly.

Eyes strictly ahead, she hurried out without waiting for an answer. She had no idea where she was heading until she found herself back at the Grenier house, hovering by the dew-perfumed shrubs at the entrance to the drive.

The house gave nothing away. Its front door stood closed and secret against her. The setting sun flared on its windows, hiding anything that might be going on within. Ned's Saab still waited in front of it, still possessed by it.

Must she walk boldly up to that brass-ornamented door and press the black button in the middle of that round brass bell-push? Yes, she must. She gathered all her courage, and murmured to herself the French she would need for whoever answered.

'*Je cherche Monsieur Flavell. Monsieur Nathan Flavell . . .*'

She broke off with a shiver. Those were the exact words she had used last night, and for the same purpose. It seemed as if France in general, and the Greniers in particular, were determined to take Ned away from her.

Well, she wasn't going to let them. '*Je cherche Monsieur Flavell*,' she announced loudly to the softening sky and, with more boldness than she felt, stepped on to the perfect asphalt of the drive.

At the same moment, one of the garages opened with a luxurious, electronic hum. The acid yellow of French headlights cut through the red sunlight, and an orange-gold car nosed down the drive. It halted next to Rachel for its driver to lean across the passenger seat and call through the open window.

'You will not find 'im 'ere,' Claudette Grenier announced smugly. 'And where 'e is, I will not tell.'

Rachel never knew how she found the strength, or the determination, for what she did next. It just seemed to happen without her conscious will. One moment she stood helpless beside the car, the next she had flung open its door, sprung into its passenger-seat, and grabbed its owner by the wrists.

A part of her noted how slender they were. She could feel their tendons moving and flexing in her grip as the small hands fluttered and furled like captive butterflies. It was no contest; she was much the stronger.

'You'll tell,' hissed this new Rachel. 'Or I'll...' Her speeded-up mind presented her with the methods of Madame Robert. 'Or I'll see your mother about what you were up to last night.'

A kitten-squeak of dismay, and Claudette stopped struggling. 'I did nozzing last night.'

'Try telling Madame Robert that. Or Ned, when I find him.'

During the long pause that followed, the small hands drooped and stilled over the imprisoned wrists. Rachel first relaxed her grip, then let them go. They fluttered to the driving-wheel, and settled there.

'We go to 'im,' Claudette announced with sudden decision.

'Where is he, then?' Rachel asked, alarmed at the idea of Ned still lost to her somewhere in this blood-red sunset.

Claudette nosed the car forward a yard or two, and swung into the road. 'At the Tour des Chats.'

'Ten miles away?' Rachel managed to conceal her dismay.

'The real Tour des Chats is nearer. The farm 'as its name and its land from a...' Brow wrinkled, Claudette searched for English words as she tortured her gears. 'A old castle, *en ruines*. Very *'istorique*...'

'And Ned wanted to look round it.' Rachel softened with love for Ned's endless, eager, curiosity, even while she fumed at the worry he had caused her. 'And he said he'd walk the rest of the way after he'd finished.'

Claudette nodded, eyes on the road.

'But couldn't he have sent a message?'

As soon as it was out, Rachel realised the question was a mistake. She should have held her peace, not uttered the least criticism of Ned, not offered the least opening for mischief.

She glanced sideways at the neat, sweet profile. Was there a new stillness in it, a new scheme hatching? And yet, the answer to her question was brutally straightforward.

''e ask me to tell you 'e will be late.'

Rachel blinked. 'So why didn't you?'

'I do not bother myself with such matters,' was the lofty reply. 'Per'aps later, when I am less busy——'

'Why, you little...' Rachel broke off, gathering her wits. 'Ned would never trust you with a message for me.'

'No?' The girl turned to her. 'But you do not know——' the car swerved, and she hauled at the wheel to straighten it '—about Ned and me.'

Rachel waited. She wasn't about to give this little madam the satisfaction of asking what 'Ned and me' meant. Her scalp prickled with foreboding, but she held her tongue and, sure enough, Claudette went on without prompting.

'Today, we 'ad the most charming *cinq-à-sept*. You 'ave 'eard of the *cinq-à-sept*?'

The five-to-seven? Rachel's mind translated the numbers, but she stayed silent.

'In France, they are the hours of love,' Claudette informed her. 'You would not understand such love, you English ... feesh.'

'Feesh'? Rachel puzzled over the word as if it mattered, and slowly realised that she was being called a fish. Well, if that meant staying cool, she would live up to it. She consciously loosened all her muscles, breathed deep, and stared down at where her hands lay deceptively quiet on her lap. When she was sure she could do it, she turned the same cool stare on her companion.

Claudette was wearing brown today—a patterned brown dress and a filmy brown scarf over her pale hair. The red-gold sunset flickered through the trees, dazzling and darkening and dazzling again through the sun-roof, lighting to orange-gold the silky hair fluttering under the brown scarf.

'Like a butterfly,' Rachel murmured to herself. 'That's what she reminds me of—the devil's butterfly.'

'*Pardon*?'

'You're lying.'

'I am not.' The pink mouth half opened; the long eyes, still focused on the darkening road, half closed. 'In the Tour des Chats is a bed of moss. On that 'e spread 'is coat for me.'

Rachel forced her hands to stay peaceful in her lap. It might be true—her stomach lurched at the idea—but it probably wasn't. It probably wasn't, it probably wasn't. She must hold on to that, hard.

'He isn't wearing a coat,' she pointed out as neutrally as she could manage.

''is suit-jacket,' the girl shot back impatiently, steering into a steep narrow side-road. 'The dark grey—you know it well. And now I, too, know it well.' She hummed a dreamy tune. 'It smell of lemon-flower, like 'is body.'

Rachel heard her own voice, dry and brisk as a broomstick. 'That's the aftershave I buy for him.'

But she knew she had blundered again. She never should have responded in any way to this nonsense, if it were nonsense. She shouldn't even be trying to show how absurd it was, if it really were as absurd as she hoped.

'You see?' Claudette pounced on the domestic note about the aftershave. 'You are 'is...' she paused, seeking the right word as Rachel herself always had to '...'is companion for each day,' she managed at last, a world of contempt in the term. 'The *cinq-à-sept* with Ned, it is not for you.'

'Nor for you either,' Rachel snapped before she could stop herself. 'Do you seriously expect me to believe you organised this——' she managed a satisfying contempt of her own '—this bed of moss, right under the noses of your parents?'

The girl flashed her a glance, pale hair flying, brown scarf fluttering, eyes wide with alarm in the dimness. 'You will not tell them?'

Rachel almost laughed at the way the little idiot had trapped herself. 'What if I did?'

'I would say it was untrue?'

'Which it is. You're a liar and a troublemaker, Claudette Grenier, and if you expect me to believe...'

Rachel broke off in alarm as they took a corner on the wrong side of the road. What was it Ned had told her? His voice came back to her, heated and clipped and precise.

'The road is narrow, steep and winding. Too difficult for an inexperienced driver.'

It was also, here under the deep cover of the trees, almost dark. The headlights shivered up and down as the wheels bounced over a pot-hole, and Rachel realised with dismay that the long acid-gold beam was far brighter than any natural light that could filter down to road level.

How had she got into this? How had she come to let herself be brought by this spoilt little girl to this unknown, creepy forest where anything could happen? All sorts of horrors might lurk unseen among these almost invisible trees. In this place, a road accident was the least of her worries...

No, it isn't, she scolded herself, and hurriedly clicked on the safety belt she had forgotten till now.

'You will see——' Claudette took another corner too fast '—I will show you the very moss where we lay, *cinq-à-sept*...'

'I thought you were taking me to Ned?'

But even as she spoke, Rachel saw how stupid she had been to believe it. How could they possibly find Ned in these conditions? Heaven knew why Claudette had started this journey—maybe as a mere panic reaction to the threat of talking to Madame Grenier.

'I did not invite you into my car.' Her words confirmed it. 'Now, you will go where I take you.'

Which might be to kingdom come, if she didn't calm down and concentrate on the road. Rachel deliberately slowed her own breathing, stilled her hands, and mastered her fears. When she answered, it was in a voice clearer, gentler, yet more commanding than she would ever have believed she could produce.

'We'll talk about that later. For now, just think about your driving.'

'I drive well,' the girl said wildly. 'My father will not accept it, but I drive very well.'

'Of course you do,' Rachel soothed. 'I'm most impressed. How much further have we to go?'

'The Tour des Chats is very soon now. A kilometre, perhaps.'

'And you've driven there before?'

'Many times. Today, I had a rendezvous there with Ned.'

Rachel caught her breath sharply, held it, and breathed out slowly. One thing Ned had never done was to lie to her.

Or had he? How would she know if he had? Wasn't the whole point of a lie to keep things hidden? But no, she couldn't afford to worry about that just now.

'I understand he was going much further,' she suggested evenly. 'To the farm, with your parents.'

'*Mais oui*.' It was working: Claudette was driving slower and more carefully. 'But on the way back, he asked to be put down at the Tour. We arranged it like that.'

'And you met him there? You...you made love?' Rachel almost gagged on the words, yet managed to get them out in that same low, neutral voice.

'Such love!' The car slowed yet more while Claudette stared into the yellow of the headlights, and sighed a gusty, sexy sigh. 'At first, 'e do not want to, but I take my clothes off, and then I kiss 'im 'ere.' She indicated the side of her own jaw, just under her ear. 'That make 'im wild.'

Rachel kept very still. She'd kissed Ned herself in that place, and in others—many, many others. Please, please, she prayed inside her head, please don't let her know of those others. If she knows about them, it just has to be true. She *could* have made him wild, especially after this morning, when he so much wanted to make love to me, and we weren't able to...

''e kiss my shoulders——' Claudette wriggled at what might or might not be the memory '—then my throat, then my lips. Then 'e take the flowers of my breasts, gently, so gently——'

'I get the picture.'

Rachel swallowed hard, and willed her voice to stay indifferent. At the edge of the headlights, trees and bushes went by ever slower. Perhaps soon she would be able to get out of the car, and make her own way back to town. That too had its terrors, but she'd worry about those when she had to face them.

'When we 'ad finished——' Claudette's voice in the dimness was lighter now, less husky '—I drive back to town alone. Ned follow on foot, so that no one will——'

She broke off with a scream. The headlights had picked up a tall figure, most of it a mere lighter patch of darkness, striding along the edge of the road.

'For heaven's sake,' Rachel snapped, brisk with relief, 'it's only...'

But already the figure had leapt aside, and only just in time. With nightmare slowness the car edged through where it had been, trundled off the road, and ploughed to rest in the middle of a thick, thorny bush of wild roses.

CHAPTER FIVE

'NED!' Rachel leant forward, straining against her safety belt, and tried uselessly to push open her door. 'Are you hurt?'

The engine had coughed to a standstill amid the shriek and clatter of disturbed birds. The yellow headlights cut through a blackness solid as ebony. Their beams picked up an enclosing tangle of blossoming, thorny branches, an endlessly receding vista of mossy trunks, and nothing else.

'Were you hit?' She strained round to peer through the darkness behind them. 'Oh, Ned, please say you're not hurt!'

'Rachel?' The deep voice rose in disbelief. 'What the hell are you doing up here? With a driver who ought to be...'

A bitten-off pause, and then the crackling of leaves and dry twigs through the darkness told her he was moving with his usual athletic ease. She slumped back, pushed away a prickling tendril from the dense mass at her open window, and let out a huge sigh of relief. The bonnet must have come perilously close to him, but it had missed. That sideways leap had carried him clear in time.

'Are you all right?' he called from somewhere beyond their imprisoning rose bush. 'Don't move—I'll get to you...'

'I'm fine.' She undid her safety belt and ran her hands over herself, testing. 'Not even a bruise.' Conscious of a shivering silence in the next seat, she turned towards it and lowered her voice. 'What about you? You're not hurt, are you? We were going so slow——'

'My car,' the girl hissed under her breath. 'What will Papa say about my car?'

If she worried about that, she couldn't have much wrong with her. Relieved, Rachel once more gave her full attention to Ned.

'Don't come this side,' she shouted, fearful of the thorny stems. 'You'll tear yourself to bits.'

'As if that mattered. Still, if you're in good shape——' more crackling, and his voice moved to another part of the darkness '—I'll open the driver's door instead—it's easier. Who the hell is driving, anyway?'

With distant surprise, Rachel realised that he hadn't even seen Claudette yet. No, of course he hadn't. The car had come at him round a corner through the gathering dark. Blinded by its headlights, aware of it only as a danger to be avoided, he wouldn't have recognized it or seen either of its occupants.

'Thank heaven you're so fit,' she shouted. 'I'll never grumble again about your rugby and cricket and...'

She broke off, startled by the kitten-hiss of rage from the seat next to her. She wasn't sure what the French words meant, but they certainly weren't compliments. Then they turned to almost-recognisable English.

'Crrriquette!' On Claudette's tongue, the word squeaked and clicked like some night insect. 'Rrrogbee! We are nearly killed, and zey speak of crrriquette and rrrogbee!'

Rachel bridled. 'Considering it was you who nearly——'

'Aaah!' Claudette squeaked as her door was wrenched open and the car's interior light came on. 'My paintwork!'

'It's you.' Ned spoke as if he'd already feared it. 'I might have known...' He stopped with an air of simmering restraint, and began forcing the driver's door wide open.

Rachel thought of the lurid phrases he would have thrown at her if she'd done something like this. Why wasn't he using them now? Why was he guarding his tongue? Could it be memories of a new, special love? Of love on a couch of moss, with a wayward girl who had made him the gift of her virginity?

I mustn't, must not think like this, she told herself, and stared up to where he had lowered his wide shoulders into the tiny gold beam of the interior light.

And for all her doubts, how could she not love him now? Look at him, her rescuer and friend and lover, his rangy body so sure and comforting in the blackness. He must have left his jacket and tie somewhere—trust him— and rolled his sleeves back over those gold-lit, powerful forearms. And he would long ago have unbuttoned his collar. His strong throat rose dark-gold from his shirt's light-gilded whiteness, and the faint sharpness of his lemon aftershave mingled with the night scents of the forest.

Then her gaze reached his face, and she had to swallow, hard. She'd never seen him like this before— elemental and unreadable as a forest demon. His eyes were pools of darkness under the dark-gold forehead and dark-gleaming, wind-blown hair. His jutting nose had a dark-gold edge; his cheekbones rose dark-gold over black valleys of shadow. His square jaw picked up more of the gold light, but showed his mouth a grim line. When he spoke again, it still wasn't to her. He was still more interested in Claudette.

'Haven't you done enough damage, without trying to kill us both as well? And stop fussing about your car—that's the least of my worries.'

So much for the mad story of *cinq-à-sept* lovemaking.

But the thought was hardly complete in Rachel's mind before the gnawing doubts rushed after it. Was the story really so mad? It *could* have happened. They could have arranged to meet in the afternoon quiet of the ruined castle. Or, more likely, Claudette could have gone to him there without his agreement, and this time succeeded in tempting him...

Was that what he meant by 'enough damage'?

'Is there any trouble in this town that isn't caused by you?' he demanded of the silent girl. 'Well?' he added after another silence. 'Cat got your tongue?'

'The cats!' Claudette huddled down, suddenly nothing but a frightened little girl. 'Do you not 'ear them?'

'You mean the birds?' Rachel asked. 'I can hear barn owls.'

'They roost in the ruins of the castle,' Ned put in with a nod which might have been approving, gold light and black shadows rising and falling over those newly mysterious features. 'And there's long-eared owls, in the forest.'

'And we must have disturbed some bigger day bird,' Rachel went on, pleased to find how much she had learnt from him over the years. 'I heard it mewing just now.'

'Mewing!' Claudette's voice rose to a note of hysteria. 'It is the cat-people who mew. St Jean, 'e conquer them, but 'ere in the forest, they live still.'

'For hundreds of years?' Rachel recalled that worn carving over the church door. 'How can they possibly——?'

'The cat-people never die. Everyone knows that.'

Over the bowed, frightened head, Rachel met the darkness that was Ned's eyes. A sharp hiss told her he was drawing breath through his teeth, a sure sign of irritation.

'Look, if you'll just back out of this bush——'

'I cannot.' The brown scarf fluttered over the despairing yellow head. 'I do not think I will ever drive again.'

'All right.' The strange shadows veered and flickered once more over Ned's face as he tilted his head in command. 'Out of there, and I'll get the car back on the road for you.'

'*Non, non, non*!' Claudette anchored herself to the steering-wheel with both fists. 'In the dark the forest belong to the cat-people. Who knows what they will do?'

'So you're going to sit there till morning?' Ned demanded in growing exasperation. 'And how's Rachel supposed to get out? Does she climb over you, or does she——?'

'You would not leave me 'ere alone?' Claudette had turned to Rachel in terror.

'She most certainly will, and serve you right,' Ned growled. 'The minute I can get her out of there, we're——'

'Wait a minute, love.' Rachel silenced him with a raised hand. 'Let me try.'

She laid her arm, gold-lit in its short robin-red cotton sleeve, gently across the shoulders of the brown dress.

'Come on, silly.' She patted Claudette as she would have patted a baby with wind. 'Either you back us out of here yourself, or you let Ned do it.'

'I cannot.' The yellow head shook again, but with a slower, softer movement, the small fists loosening on the steering-wheel. 'And I cannot get out, to wait alone in the forest.'

'You won't be alone. Honestly not.' Rachel went on patting. 'I'll be there with you.'

'But you——' the yellow head turned towards her '—will be 'ere, in the car.'

'I'll get straight out after you. And until I do——' Rachel darted a glance towards the mysterious light-and-dark figure holding the door '—Ned'll be there to look after you.'

'Will I hell...' The pools of darkness stilled, the hardly visible eyes meeting Rachel's, and Ned broke off on a suppressed rumble. 'I'll be here,' he promised like a volcano not quite erupting. 'You won't be alone.'

'So you see, it's going to be all right,' Rachel soothed. 'All you have to do is get out, and you'll soon be home and laughing at yourself.'

'I would never laugh about the cat-people.'

'You'll be home,' Rachel murmured. 'What were you planning to do this evening?'

'N-nozzing.' It was like an admission of guilt. 'Since one year, zis was always our evening to be togezzaire, but now...' The girl turned to Rachel as if for support. 'Why should I not sunbaze all I wish?'

'Sunbaze...? Oh.' Rachel understood. 'With no clothes on?'

'I must stop, 'e say. 'Oo is 'e, to say I must stop?'

Hadn't Madame Robert said that Claudette had some regular admirer with whom she had quarrelled? Was that why she'd thrown herself at Ned?

'I 'ate 'im!' She had raised her head to shoot a conniving glance at Ned. 'I will tell 'im about you and me. 'e will be very jealous——'

'Come on.' Ned's great hands grabbed the small ones from the wheel and drew them after him, straightening to his full six feet three. 'Out you come.'

And out Claudette came. Smoothly and gracefully, she rose with the gold-lined shadow that was Ned, and flowed into it so that the two shadows were one.

Rachel gazed up in dismay at that single shadow which was really two. What had she done, throwing them together like this? And yet, what else could she have done?

'Hurry up, Jel.'

Was Ned's voice throatier than usual? Was he responding against his will to the sweetly curved young body so close to his? Was this how he had responded this afternoon, in the castle, on that bed of moss...?

'Coming.'

Rachel scrambled over the driving seat and out into the rose-scented night. The minute she was upright he thrust Claudette at her like something too hot to handle.

'Over to you.'

With the speed and suppleness always so striking in one of his size, he lowered himself to the driving seat. Claudette uttered another squeak as the door shut and the light went out, and Rachel resumed her job of soothing away night fears.

'Nearly done.' She patted the trembling, unresponsive shoulder. 'The hardest part's over already.'

And she could really begin to hope that it was. Already Ned had restarted the engine. The rose bush released the car with a snapping, scented sigh, the yellow of the headlights cut through the night for a blinding moment or two, and then the car was back on the road, facing down the way it had come.

'Get in, Jel,' Ned called from the driving-seat window. 'Sit next to me, and we'll put madam there in the back.'

'What?' Claudette stalked the short distance to the road with crackling, outraged speed. 'You would make me ride in the back seat of my own car?' She bent to the driving-seat window, a black figure against the yellow of the headlights. 'For what do you take me, Monsieur Ned?'

'What I take you for,' Ned's deep voice hissed from somewhere above the lit dashboard, 'is a...' he broke off, and finished on a new note, almost of resignation '...is another question. I can't drive off and leave you here—your father wouldn't like it,' he went on. 'So get in the back, there's a good girl.'

Rachel plodded up to join them on the road, her feet sinking and snapping among last year's leaves and fallen twigs. What, she wondered drearily, had Ned really meant to call Claudette? A mantrap—that was one of the names he'd used at some time or other. Had the mantrap now caught him, her own and only man? Was that why he no longer felt he could say the word aloud? To distract herself from such thoughts, she joined in the argument.

'Come on, Claudette.' She worked to keep her voice calm and reasonable, though she couldn't prevent it trembling a little. 'You said yourself you didn't want to drive any more——'

'I did not; I 'ave nevaire said such a thing.' The girl whirled on her. 'Of course I can drive!'

'But...but you did say it. I heard you.' Rachel paused, bewildered by the denial. 'And you nearly killed us all. If I hadn't made you slow down...if Ned hadn't jumped——'

'Get in, both of you,' Ned ordered. 'Or I'll come out there and make you.'

'Do zat.' Claudette's shadow against the headlights drew itself up, hands on hips, elbows wide. 'Come out and make me.'

Rachel looked from one to the other in the black-and-yellow dimness. Here on the road the immovable object; there in the car the invisible, irresistible force. At this rate, they'd never get back to town.

'At least let her sit in the front, Ned,' she pleaded. 'I don't mind the back.'

'No,' the invisible Ned announced with finality. 'You don't know the tricks she gets up to.'

'T-tricks?' Rachel swallowed back sudden tears. 'So she really did——?'

'Did what?' His quick ear had at once caught the break in her voice. 'Carry on like a tart? Don't take on about it, Jel; you know what she's like.'

'All right,' Rachel sniffled, suddenly weary to death. 'I won't take on about it.'

She wouldn't cry—not here, not now. She shut her eyes tight, and heard without understanding the click of the car door opening. A rush of air brushed her face as he moved to her, and then here he was, the scent of lemon all round her, his dear arms walling her in, his dear voice murmuring for her only.

'Now then, Jel!' His breath fanned her ear. 'You were so good, back there after the accident...'

'Was I?' She raised her eyes, found nothing but blackness, and drooped thankfully to the lemon-scented paleness of his shirt. 'Was I really, Ned?'

'Kept your head, dealt with every problem as it came.' His arms closed her in tight. 'Just keep it up for a little longer now, hm?'

'I'll... I'll try.'

She blinked, and sniffed hard. One tear spilled down her cheek, but it was all right—his lips wiped it away.

'That's my girl...'

A new and sinister noise cut him short. An engine fired and purred, wheels turned, and the car moved away in a pungent cloud of exhaust fumes.

Ned sprang apart from Rachel with one of his usual curses. She heard his light shoes pounding the road, and saw his great shadow, outlined now by the red glow of the tail-lights, spring downhill, away from her and after the car.

But already he was much too late. The tail-lights winked derisively, lit the edge of the forest a brief, fiery red, and vanished round the curve.

'The little... *louse*!' Rachel gasped, when at last she took in what had happened. 'To leave us up here...'

'Let's just hope she gets back in one piece.'

Ned's voice through the darkness showed that he was returning up the hill. He didn't sound at all breathless from his brief sprint, and not nearly as put out as he should have been.

'And the car too, of course,' he added with the same maddening calm.

'What the hell does it matter about the... the wretched car?' Rachel reined in her desire to use language as forceful as his. 'It's her own fault if she wrecks it, and anyway, didn't you say it was the least of your worries?'

'No, I didn't.'

'Is everybody going mad?' she demanded, utterly bewildered. 'I heard you myself, plain as daylight...' She broke off, and huddled her arms across her body.

Daylight, she thought with sudden longing. Oh, to have a bit of daylight common sense on all this!

Suddenly she could perfectly understand Claudette's fear of the enormous, rustling night of the forest. In this whispering blackness, anything could happen. Any plain statement could be turned upside-down, any fact denied.

'What I said,' Ned—a looming shadow against the paler darkness of the sky—began, 'applied to the paintwork only.'

'So you do care about the rest of it,' Rachel accused wildly. 'And about her too, I suppose...'

'Don't be silly.'

But his voice was tender. She let him draw her close again, and yielded to his sheltering hands, one at the back of her waist, the other smoothing her hair from her face. He was right—she *was* being silly. How could she ever have distrusted him, her Ned whom she'd known all her life?

Only I haven't, not really, her mind threw back at her. He's full of ideas I didn't know about, feelings I didn't know about. He's not my Ned at all.

'We couldn't help her leaving us,' he went on with an air of having settled one problem and now turning to another. 'And I'm sure she'll manage the short way back all right——'

'You see, you *do* care.' Rachel stiffened against him, and tried to draw away. 'You care far more about her getting back safely than about us, stuck here with miles to walk——'

'Two miles, to be exact. We can do it in half an hour.' He held on to her waist, refusing to let her go. 'Until that damned car came at me, I was enjoying the walk.'

'It was light then; it's dark now,' she pointed out to his glimmering white shirt. 'What've you done with your jacket and tie, by the way?'

'Left them in the Grenier car. And it isn't dark. Look.'

His fingers lifted her chin, forcing her to look up. She saw with wonder that he was right. She'd never noticed while the various car lights were glaring, but the sky now sparkled with stars, a near-full moon high among them like a pearl on silver-dusted black silk. She lowered her gaze to the road ahead and sure enough she could see it plain—a blue-white pathway through velvet-black shadows.

'Can we or can't we,' he demanded, 'walk back by that light?'

'Stop trying to change the subject.' She pushed at his chest in a new, vain attempt to free herself. 'Exactly what is Claudette Grenier to you?'

His snort lifted the hair at the top of her head, and yet, incredibly, it seemed as much of amusement as of anger. 'Let's just say that as long as she gets home safe I'm glad to see the back of her.'

Rachel's heart twisted, but she couldn't voice her real fear. She couldn't ask outright *why* he was glad to see the back of Claudette Grenier. And not for anything could she have suggested the possible, awful reason that the girl was a constant reminder of his own unfaithfulness.

'So it does matter to you,' she persisted, the nearest she could come to expressing her thoughts, 'that Claudette arrives home safe?'

'Doesn't it to you?' He now had a firm grip on her waist with both hands, a hard circle of logic against the chaos of her fears. 'Claudette's a world-class pain in the ... neck——' he clearly meant a much ruder word '—but you can't want her in a car smash any more than I do.'

'Of course not!'

Rachel shook her head, surprised at her own vehemence. He was right as ever and, as ever, one step ahead of her. No matter how much trouble the girl had caused, the thought of a road accident was still a horrifying one.

'Well, we did our best to help.' His hands relaxed, their message received. 'I tried to drive that dinky-toy car back safe. I still want it safe...'

'Because it's hers?' Rachel's doubts rushed in anew.

'Because, if it isn't, Monsieur Grenier pays. Which won't be good for his temper, or——' Ned spoke slowly and clearly, making sure she took it in '—for our bargaining.'

'I see.' She stood with her hands on his chest, seeking comfort from its warmth and power and finding none. 'So we're back to business again.'

'We never left it.'

'No.' She bowed her head, overcome by immense fatigue. 'We never do.'

'Now there I disagree.'

And the infuriating man kissed her, full on the lips. She tried to pull away, but he wouldn't let her, claimed all of her mouth with all of his, and held it until she gradually, reluctantly responded. His hard lips probed hers, seeking, finding, parting to let his tongue meet and dominate hers. Only when his hands began to claim her body did she manage to struggle free, and even then he made it seem like his idea.

TAKE 4 MEDICAL ROMANCES *FREE*

Mills & Boon Medical Romances capture all the excitement, intrigue and emotion of a busy medical world. But a world never too busy to ignore love and romance.

We will send you four Medical Romances plus a cuddly Teddy and a mystery gift absolutely FREE, as your introduction to this superb series.

At the same time we'll reserve a subscription for you to our Reader Service. Every month you could receive the latest four Medical Romances delivered direct to your door Postage and Packing FREE, plus our FREE Newsletter packed with author news, competitions, special offers and much more.

What's more, there's no obligation. You may cancel or suspend your subscription at any time. So you've nothing to lose and a whole world of romance to gain!

YOUR GIFT

Return this card today and we'll send you this lovely cuddly Teddy Bear absolutely FREE.

Fill in the Free Books Certificate overleaf ▼ ▼

Free Books Certificate

Yes! Please send me four FREE Medical Romances, together with my FREE cuddly Teddy and mystery gift. Please also reserve a special Reader Service subscription for me. If I decide to subscribe, I shall receive four brand new books every month for just £6.80, postage and packing FREE. If I decide not to subscribe, I shall write to you within 10 days. Any free books and gifts will be mine to keep in any case.
I understand that I am under no obligation whatsoever - I may cancel or suspend my subscription at any time simply by writing to you.
I am over 18 years of age.

Your Extra Bonus Gift

We all love mysteries, so as well as the books and cuddly Teddy we've an intriguing gift just for you. No clues - send off today!

5A3D

Ms/Mrs/Miss/Mr _____

Address _____

_____

_____

Postcode _____ Signature _____

NO STAMP
NEEDED

Mills & Boon
Reader Service
FREEPOST
PO Box 236
Croydon
CR9 9EL

▲ **Send No Money Now**

'Ah, well...' He released her with a husky laugh. 'After all, this isn't the place.'

'The place for what?' But her own hot longing told her exactly what he meant, and she couldn't pretend. 'It certainly isn't,' she agreed, 'or the time either. Have you forgotten—— ?'

'I've forgotten nothing.' His hair moon-silvered, his strong features lit now with silver instead of gold, he reached for her hand. 'Come on——' he started downhill, preparing to swing into his rhythmic, long-distance walk '—we can talk on our way back to town.'

She resisted, pulling away from that warm, enclosing hand, planting her feet on the road and leaning back-wards in her effort not to move. 'I don't *want* to walk back to town. Do we absolutely have to?'

'Not absolutely.' He kept her hand but waited, pre-pared to hear her. 'I thought you'd enjoy it.'

'Well, I wouldn't. I've walked miles today already. All by myself,' she added, unable to resist reminding him of it.

'Now, Jel,' he warned. 'We've had all that.'

'What?' She could hardly believe her ears. 'You promised to be back at six, and here you still are,' she reminded him. 'I was going frantic——'

'You were what?' His stillness was suddenly intense. 'Didn't you get my message?'

Rachel's heart sank. He really had sent a message through Claudette, as the girl had claimed. Then maybe the rest of the story was true also. Maybe he *had* broken faith, made love to another woman...

'How could you, Ned?' Rachel struggled to keep the break out of her voice. 'With her of all people...'

'How could I what? And with whom?' He sounded genuinely bewildered. 'You're not making sense, Jel.'

Rachel gulped, and tried to put her fears into words. 'How could you...' But it was no good—she couldn't speak of it. She gave up, and finished weakly, 'How could you ever rely on Claudette Grenier to deliver a message?'

'What?' The volcano erupted at last with a roar that set up a startled, answering fluster of sleepy birds in the forest. 'Are you out of your mind? Would I ever do a thing like that?'

'It's what she said...'

'And you believed her?' He grabbed Rachel's hair, and knocked the cushion of his thumb softly up and down on her head. 'What've you got in there—cotton-wool? As if I'd ever——'

'Ouch!' It was her own jerking attempt to free herself that hurt her, but she made the most of it. 'Would you kindly leave my hair alone?'

'Eh? Oh.' He slid his hand along the tress and held it up, wondering how it had got there. 'Sorry. But as if I'd ever——'

'All right, all right,' she admitted hurriedly. 'Maybe I shouldn't have believed her. I *told* her I didn't...'

'That's something, I suppose. Honestly, Jel!'

'I'm sorry!' But as soon as she heard herself, she turned away from him in fury. 'How come I'm the one who's apologising? You must have sent that wretched message all wrong...'

'I sent two.' His one hand held her with ease, his other pulling her round to face him again. 'One via the Greniers when they dropped me off at the castle——'

'So you really did explore the Tour des Chats?' she choked, hating the thought of what else he might have done there.

'Now what's eating you?'

She didn't answer, head lowered and eyes on that glimmering, unbuttoned shirt.

He took her chin once more, and forced her head up. 'Is it because I went over the castle without you?'

She looked sideways at the velvet-shadowed trees, anywhere but at him, and tried to laugh. 'You could say that.'

'Such a fuss.' The irritated breath hissed through his teeth. 'I'll take you there tomorrow—will that do?'

'No!' She so much didn't want to see that couch of moss that the horrified exclamation was out before she could control it. 'I mean . . .'

'Either you want to go over it, or you don't.'

The exasperation had reached his voice now, and no wonder. From his point of view, Rachel admitted to herself, she was making no sense at all. Besides, wasn't his very unawareness a proof that he had nothing to hide? She gathered her wits.

'Bother the castle!' She pulled her chin free of his controlling hand. 'What about these messages that didn't arrive? One by the Greniers, you said?'

He nodded. 'They promised to warn you I'd be a bit later than I thought.'

'A bit? I waited *hours*!'

'Yes, well, I'll tell you about that in a minute. The Greniers must have sent on the warning via Claudette.' He shook his moon-silvered head at such incompetence. 'Why the hell didn't they just open the window and ask the sparrows to do the job?'

'Or the butterflies,' Rachel murmured.

'The what?' But he didn't really want to know, still working on the problem of the vanishing messages. 'Then I rang Madame Robert at the bar, about——' he glanced at his watch '—about an hour ago. You didn't get that either?'

'By then I'd gone out looking for you.'

'To the Greniers'? That was sensible.'

She felt an inner glow. In spite of her fatigue, in spite of her suspicions, in spite of everything he'd done or might have done, praise from Ned was still something to be treasured and worked for.

'Only,' he added, 'why didn't they straighten you out about where I was, and look after you till I got back?'

'Because I met Claudette and never reached them,' Rachel explained. 'And you know how infuriating she can be——'

'Don't I just!'

The heartfelt exclamation started a host of new, ugly fears. Yes, he found Claudette infuriating—and what else? Sexy? Irresistible? Able to get through his guard exactly as he himself could get through Rachel's even when he'd made her angry?

'Go on, Jel,' he ordered impatiently. 'You still haven't told me how you came to be in the car with her.'

'Oh. Well. I suppose,' she began unwillingly, 'I rather, sort of—er—boarded it. And made her tell me where you were.'

'Good for you.'

'You think so?'

She basked once more in his approval. When she dared to look at him, his eyes were still in shadow. However, the silvered crinkles at their edges, the silvered gentleness of his jaw, the upturned corners of his mouth, all showed that he understood and sympathised with what she had done.

'Except she never would, of course,' he added, spoiling it. 'Even if she knew. Which, at that time, she didn't.'

'At that time, at that time'—the words pounded in Rachel's brain. There had been a time when Claudette did know where he was. Had she used that knowledge...?

I won't think like this, Rachel told herself, I won't.

But the effort not to was enormous. It wore her out, so that she wanted nothing but to lie down, and rest her aching head, and be peaceful, and not think any more at all. And what a long way they had to go before she could do that.

'I suppose we'd better get moving,' she said drearily, and tried to set off down the road back to town.

His arm shot out to grab her, and he stayed where he was. 'Not that way.'

'What?' She turned impatiently. 'What other way is there?'

'You said you didn't want to walk back—remember?'

'If wishes were horses...'

'Stop trying to run things, and listen.' He hauled her towards him, and took her hand. 'We're going the other way.'

'Uphill? Further into the forest?'

She peered fearfully along the uphill track. Where it disappeared round the next bend, the trees seemed to close over it entirely. She hoped it was an optical illusion. She hoped so very much because, if Ned meant them to go uphill, uphill was where they would go.

'Only about quarter of a mile.' Sure enough he was setting off, still holding her hand so that she had to pad along at his side in her trainers.

'But where are we going?' she asked, trying not to sound as anxious as she felt.

'You'll see.' He dropped her hand, but only so he could catch her waist and draw her closer. 'That's my Jel——' his fingers smoothed the moon-darkened cotton of her T-shirt '—dressed just right for the job. Madame Grenier was in stilt heels at the farm this afternoon.'

'Yes, well——' she tried to resist '—this isn't what I hoped I'd be wearing this evening.'

It wasn't an optical illusion. Here at the next corner, the trees really did close overhead. Rachel gave up resisting, glad to let herself be drawn as near as possible to his warm, protective strength. She jumped, and trembled, as the barn owl's weird shriek sounded again among the trees.

'I wish you'd tell me why we're doing this...'

'Nearly there,' he soothed. 'What *did* you hope to wear this evening, then?'

He was humouring her, she knew. As long as her clothes were practical for out of doors, he cared no more about her wardrobe than about his own. Nevertheless, she seized on the distraction.

'I put on that amber dress you like.'

'The traffic-light one?' In the gloom above her head he let out a curling, sexy whistle. 'The one that says get ready to go?'

At any other time she might have told him not to be so vulgar. Here, in the speckled dark under the trees, she could only be grateful, and press closer to his fearless vitality.

'Pity,' he said, his fingers warm on her waist.

'I thought so too,' she agreed as she remembered her careful, wasted preparations.

'Still, there's always tomorrow. By then, we'll really have something to celebrate.'

'You haven't got the contract yet,' she reminded him.

'I will have by then, and more besides. Lots more.'

'Like what?'

'You'll know when I've got it.'

'You're so damn sure of yourself...' Her foot caught in an invisible pot-hole, and she had to accept his steadying hand. 'Exactly why,' she burst out in rebellion, 'are we stumbling round here in the back of beyond?'

'Hang on to me.' He kept hold of her hand, supporting her with loving care. 'I'm not stumbling.'

'You wouldn't be...'

'And this isn't the back of beyond either, not really,' he went on in perfect good humour. 'At certain times, lots of people come this way.'

'Then I wish this were one of those times.'

'No, you don't.' He guided her round the corner, out into the next patch of moonlight. 'You don't want crowds of people. All you want is me.'

And it was so true that the fight drained out of her. She sighed, and kept pace with him on the white velvet-shadowed road, and wished it weren't so, but it was. Whatever he might have done this afternoon, whatever discomforts he had in store for her now, she couldn't change her feelings. All she wanted was him.

CHAPTER SIX

ALL the same, Rachel decided, a person had to have her say now and then. By this time it must be quite ten minutes that she'd dragged along beside Ned, ever wearier, ever more impatient, ever more fearful that this moonlit road would just go on winding uphill to the end of the world.

'So where *are* we going?' she asked, determined at last to have an answer. 'As far as I can see, it's just further and further into...'

She stopped, and blinked. One minute there'd been only forest, and road, and a little sky. Now they'd rounded a corner, and here, like magic, stretched a long, low building, bright with curtained windows and cheerful with geranium-filled window boxes.

'What...what are you doing to me, Ned Flavell?' she stammered. 'Dragging me through a haunted forest, to a house that appears out of nowhere...'

'It's real.' He walked her through an ancient gateway into a stone-flagged courtyard. 'Though it's more than just a house.' He pointed to the name in gold letters over the well-lit massive door. 'It's the Auberge des Chats,' he told her, pleased with his surprise.

Beyond the courtyard, stone walls loomed away into moon-silvered darkness. Here, however, the darkness was banished by more of those bright, flowered windows, and by lamps either side of the door.

On the other hand, the lamps on the white outdoor tables were all dark.

'It looks nice,' Rachel said doubtfully. 'But is it open? Nobody's eating, and——' she indicated the tables '—all the chairs are tipped up.'

'That's because it's after dark. Though I admit I expected it to be busier.' He made for the door. 'It was pretty popular this afternoon when I was here.'

'This afternoon? Was that before or after the...' but no, she wouldn't speak the fearful words 'cinq-à-sept', she would not '...the castle?' she finished, stumbling wearily after him over the stone flags.

He paused to let her catch up, and took her elbow to guide and support her. 'This *is* the castle.'

'What?' She halted with him at the doorstep. 'But I said I didn't want to come here.'

'You said no such thing.' He turned to look down at her, his shaggy brows drawn together in disagreement. 'The opposite, in fact. You sulked because I came here without you.'

'I did not! I couldn't have, I'd never...'

She bit back the rest. 'I'd never want to see the place where you were unfaithful,' she'd almost said.

'Anyway,' she began instead, staring at the well-maintained dark wood of the door in its mortared-stone surround, 'I thought the castle was in ruins.'

'It is.' He lifted a wrought-iron knocker shaped like an arched-up cat, and thudded it down twice. 'This place was built into the gatehouse about a hundred years ago, specifically as an inn.'

'And people come here to it? Through that haunted forest?'

'In droves.'

'Well, they aren't here now,' she pointed out with gloomy satisfaction.

Her doubts proved justified. The door opened to reveal a queenly old lady, all alone in a wide, dim, stone-flagged corridor. When she saw them her hands flew to remove her white apron, then fluttered with unnecessary tidying gestures at her piled-up white hair.

'*Bonsoir*, Monsieur Flavell,' she began with surprised warmth and, as an afterthought, '*Bonsoir, mademoiselle.*'

'*Bonsoir, madame,*' Rachel returned automatically before hissing to Ned, 'She knows you?'

He didn't answer. He was listening to the old lady, who was now telling them that, sadly, the restaurant was closed this evening. She added in lilting, southern French that not even for Monsieur Flavell could she expect her husband to sacrifice his television football.

Ned immediately launched on some discussion Rachel could barely understand. She caught the name Étienne, and understood that this person interested himself neither in television nor in football. Then she lost track, until the now beaming old lady led them to a telephone at the end of the corridor, and bustled off.

'Is this so you can ring for a taxi?' Rachel asked.

He paused, hand on the receiver. 'Do you want to freshen up?'

'Wouldn't hurt, I suppose.' She started for the door marked '*Toilettes*', and paused. 'How long will the taxi be, d'you think? I'm hungry,' she realised with surprise, 'and, at this rate, it's going to be an awful long time before we——'

'We're eating here.'

'What?' She paused, bewildered. 'But *madame* said——'

'Her son's cooking for us.'

'Is that the Étienne you were on about?'

He nodded, busy dialling.

'You might have told me,' she snapped, hunger-goaded.

'I'm telling you now, aren't I? The restaurant's through there.' He indicated a majestic, double-leafed door, and turned his back on her. 'See you inside.'

And she did, at a corner table with its own red-shaded lamp. Beneath the lamp, silver cutlery glittered on a cloth of figured white damask. Beyond that single circle of light, rosy shadows stretched ever darker, along wood panelling studded with other, unlit lamps. Apart from themselves, the restaurant was empty.

'You know what——' he rose with unusual formality, reached her side of the table before she did, and pulled out a chair for her '—you look smashing.'

'Do I?' She'd been about to sit, but lingered facing him, nervously fingering a strand of her long dark hair. 'I didn't have a comb, and I'm not wearing any make-up...'

'Good. We don't need those things.'

'What d'you mean, "we"? *I'm* the one who——'

'Leave your hair alone.' The deep voice stroked her like velvet. 'It's perfect the way it is.'

Rachel dropped her gaze to the white-and-silver of the table, and babbled any nonsense that came into her head. 'I did a full make-up for the traffic-light dress, but then I washed it off...' She had to stop; her throat had closed.

'You're perfect.' His hands caught hers, stilling and subduing. 'All of you.'

She darted her tongue out to moisten her lips, and heard him catch his breath. Oh, dear, why was he doing this to her? She turned her head sharply away, determined not to let him kiss her, and tried to pull her hands from his.

He wouldn't let them go. Instead he turned them inexorably over, raised them to his lips, and kissed the hollow of each palm. Needles of mind-drugging pleasure inched through her from the contact, but she dragged in a long painful breath, and forced her voice out.

'Wh-why the compliments?'

'They aren't compliments, they're the simple truth.' The wide shirt-clad shoulders at the edge of her field of vision rose and fell in a magnificent shrug. 'I'm just saying I like you. Is that so strange?'

'Well...' She tried once more to free her hand from his, and failed. 'You don't say that sort of thing every day.'

'Maybe I should.'

'Well, but if you did, you wouldn't be...'

She trailed off. You wouldn't be my Ned, she'd wanted to say, but couldn't. He wasn't her Ned anyway. He never had been, whatever she had once believed. On that chilling thought, she at last dared to raise her eyes to his.

And those steel-blue eyes at once cast their familiar spell. Now that they had her, she knew they wouldn't let her go. She was his until he chose to release her.

Defying them, held by them, she saw that they weren't steel-blue at all, not tonight. A distant logic told her it was the rosy shadows from the lamp which changed their colour almost to violet, but it didn't help. The same shadows brought out strange bronze highlights in the gold-gleaming hair, softened the high cheekbones, and touched the hard mouth to a gentleness she hardly recognised.

She was still trying to recognise it when it claimed hers.

At first it merely caressed the outer curves of her lips. Then it hardened, demanded, probed, his body surging to hers. She made a wordless noise of distress, but when she tried to pull back she had her own eager body to fight, its melting, answering pulses too powerful to resist.

It was Ned who finally broke away, breathing hard and almost pushing her from him. 'Will you stop doing that?'

'Doing what?' She dropped to her chair, glad to be off her shaky legs. 'You're the one who——'

'On second thoughts, don't stop.' He seated himself lightly in the chair opposite, and laid his hands flat on the table before him. 'I wouldn't have you any different.'

'I don't know what's got into you tonight...'

But she couldn't go on. Maybe, after all, she did know what had got into him. Maybe he'd found a new appetite, one roused by another woman, which only focused on herself because she happened to be there. Was that why his voice came out so low, so not-quite-in-control? Was that why he was speaking so rapidly, grabbing at any idea that might distract them both?

And what on earth *was* he talking about now? Had she heard right? she wondered as she patted and smoothed the robin-red T-shirt and tried to quiet the beating of her heart beneath it. 'Were you saying something about a cat?'

Still husky, he laughed and swung sideways to glance over his shoulder. 'I was asking if you'd noticed it.'

She peered into the shadows at the various objects which decorated the walls. A stag's head on a wooden plaque, a furry pelt that might have belonged to a wolf, and over there—yes, this must be what he meant. In the place of honour over the window, a tabby-striped cat snarled from a wedge of similarly striped granite.

'Poor darling.' Rachel stared at it, then realised why it had been made to seem so ferocious. 'Is it a wild one?'

'*Felis silvestris*,' Ned confirmed, and picked up the wine bottle with a well-steadied hand. 'They're still about in this forest, I believe.'

'So that's why Claudette was making all the fuss...' Rachel broke off, miserable to have mentioned the wretched girl at this time of all times.

'Fuss is the word.' Was his agreement too hasty? 'They've far more to fear from us than we have from them.'

He poured a little wine into his own glass and tasted it. Then he poured hers, and went on talking about wild cats. Was he covering up? Was all this chat designed simply to push their talk away from dangerous ground?

I won't think about it, Rachel told herself for the twentieth time. She sipped her wine, and did her best to hear what he was telling her. He'd somehow got on to the fifth-century St Jean.

'...maybe converted an ancient tribe of cat worshippers to Christianity,' he was speculating. 'And over the years, that grew into the legend about his driving all the cats away... ah.' He sat back in—was it relief? 'This looks like our first course.'

And it was. The glossy asparagus was brought in by a smiling, very young man in a snow-white, high-necked jacket, a chef's hat tall on his dark head.

'Jel, this is Étienne Lebrun,' Ned introduced them. 'And this, Étienne,' he continued in slow, very clear English, 'is my girl, Rachel.'

'*Enchanté, madame.*' The young man bowed shyly over Rachel's hand. '*J'espère que——*'

'English, Étienne,' Ned instructed with fatherly firmness. 'You should be practising every chance you get.'

'I 'ope you will enjoy ze dinner I prepare for you,' Étienne intoned like a good, obedient pupil, 'and zat it will be ze first of many.'

'I—er—hope so too,' Rachel murmured, and waited until they were alone again before she turned to Ned. 'What does he mean, the first of many?'

'Have some asparagus.' He piled it on her plate. 'Notice the pinkish tips? That's how the French like it— they say we English eat it before it's ripe.'

Rachel opened her mouth for more questions. Before she could say a word he had popped a choice, hollandaise-dripping asparagus spear into it, and her tongue had to curl round it and savour it as it deserved.

'Isn't it good!' she exclaimed when she could speak again.

She took another, and for an indefinite, delightful time spoke no more. Only when every luscious, perfect shoot was gone, all the rich, sharply satisfying sauce used up, did she think again of her questions.

'What did your nice friend mean by "the first of many"? Will we be eating here again?'

'Maybe, but that's not what he meant.' Ned leant back, and sipped his wine. 'He's coming to work in Flavell's.'

'Goodness! When did you fix that?'

'This afternoon. I dropped in for a beer after I'd finished at the Tour, and we got talking.'

Étienne, it seemed, had been to a famous catering college, and was anxious to show what he could do. His papa, however, ruled supreme in the kitchen here, and frowned on changes. So what could be more satisfactory to all than that Étienne should give England the benefit of his newly acquired skills, and at the same time polish his English?

'And seeing the Caster restaurant needs somebody,' Ned finished, 'I took him on. Then I realised how late it was, and rang Madame Robert from here.'

Rachel went over the story in her mind, and found it added up. 'So that,' she began as hope slowly revived her, 'is what you were doing while I paced the floor at the Hotel du Centre?'

'In your get-ready-to-go dress?' He eyed her curves with enjoyment. 'That must have been quite a sight.'

'I suppose so.' She remembered her attempt to go downstairs. 'The men in the bar certainly thought so.'

'What?' The gold-glinting head shot up, shaggy brows drawn together over the high-bridged, assertive nose. 'You went in the bar in that gear? Alone?'

'Well . . .' She broke off, determined not to tell him of her hasty retreat. 'What if I did?' she snapped instead. 'What am I supposed to do, stand in a corner till you can spare me a minute?'

'Did any of them . . . ?' He paused, correcting himself. '*How many* of them made a play for you?' He leant over the table, fists clenched. 'Maybe that's what you wanted?'

'And . . . and what if I did?' she gasped. 'Talk about double standards . . .'

'Double standards be damned!' His growl was thunderous. 'Any man can enjoy goods on offer. There's a hell of a difference between that, and you offering them!'

'I can't believe I'm hearing this!'

But she had to stop there, to let Étienne clear the empty plates. And when it was done, and they were alone again, Ned had built up a whole new head of steam.

'I see now what you were up to.' He leant forward over the cleared table, the superb muscles in his forearms tense. 'You were paying me out, weren't you?'

'It would have served you right if I...' She stopped, the fear twisting once more within her. 'Paying you out for what?'

'Mostly for Claudette, I suppose.'

'So you did...' She choked to a halt.

'Did what? Fancy her? Of course I did, same as I fancied all those girls we talked about this morning.' He made a brief noise of impatience, the square chin rising contemptuously, the bright hair tossing and settling. 'Some women are anybody's to fancy. You're not.'

The arrogance of it! 'So I'm supposed to hang about till you've done all the... the *fancying* you want.' She felt tears pricking, and sniffed them angrily back. 'Then, when you've a minute to spare, you'll get round to me.'

'What the hell are you on about now?' Was that a new watchfulness in the violet-blue eyes?

You know very well, she wanted to storm. Stop acting the innocent and pretending you don't.

But no, she didn't dare challenge him openly with Claudette's story. If it were true, it would tear her whole world apart, and just now she didn't feel strong enough to cope with that.

'I only went into the bar looking for you.' The tears almost spilled. 'If you hadn't dumped me for the day, then again for the evening, I needn't have gone near it...'

She closed her eyes, but too late. One wretched tear had got away from her, and trickled down her cheek. She scrubbed at it furiously with the back of her hand.

'Women!' A sigh blew on her from the other side of the table, and a cool, lemon-scented handkerchief mopped her cheek. 'Do stop taking on so, Jel——'

'Leave me alone.' She turned her head away, rejecting any further help from the handkerchief.

'You need food.'

She shook her head, tears flowing now in a steady stream. 'I had a very good lunch from Madame Robert.'

'A long time ago. And you've been through a lot since then.'

'And whose fault's that?'

'Come on, come on!' His fingers played over her hot, wet cheek, then took her chin and forced her to face him. 'Do you want Étienne to think I've been beating you?'

'You d-did sh-shake me,' she reminded him. 'L-last night.'

'Yes, well, I'm sorry for that.'

'Are you?' Her sobs stopped in sheer amazement at this rare, extraordinary thing: an apology from Ned Flavell. 'You really are? Really sorry?'

'You needn't make a meal of it...' A pause, and then the tear-blurred figure opposite, white and bronze, gold and violet-blue, reluctantly nodded. 'I really am. I'm also sorry that I——' it came out in a rush, to get it over '—that I had to leave you alone for so long. Now, will you promise,' he went on quickly, 'to keep your get-ready-to-go dress, and others like it, for when I'm around to look after you?'

'No!' She blinked her vision clear and faced him. 'Not unless you promise to be around a bit more.'

He froze in the act of putting his handkerchief back in his pocket. Slowly the glinting head rose, violet-blue eyes meeting hers in astonishment. She had astonished herself, but she wasn't drawing back now.

'Are you telling me,' he began boldly, 'that if I don't look after you better I might lose you?'

As if that were possible, she wanted to shout. As if I'd ever be able to accept any other man, after you... But she only held his gaze, and nodded.

'S-something like that.'

The moment went on and on. The pendulum clock on the wall ticked, and ticked, and ticked again, and still their glances stayed locked.

Then, somewhere beyond their bright circle of light, a door opened softly. Rachel turned toward it, knowing that Ned was doing the same, that their two bodies were reacting as one. Breathless, as if from lovemaking, she watched Étienne approach their table with a silver dish on which three tiny pink crayfish balanced with their tails together.

'Are—these—local, Étienne?' The words came out in short bursts, as if Ned, too, was having trouble with his breathing.

The younger man nodded solemnly, too absorbed in his own tasks to notice their tension. 'I caught them myself, *monsieur*, in the river below the farm.'

Thanking him politely, stilling her hands under the table while she waited for him to go, Rachel regained her composure. When they were once more alone, she found she could even speak of everyday things.

'Oh, dear, I never can crack things out of shells. And these are so small...'

'It's time you learnt', Ned told her as he always did. 'But give yours here. This once, I'll do it for you.'

The bite-sized pieces he extracted from the miniature shells turned out to be surprisingly choice. Nevertheless Rachel ate very little.

'So much work,' she commented as she watched him deal deftly with the final pink claw, 'for so little gain.'

'This isn't work——' he shook free another morsel '—it's pure pleasure.'

'But then, so is all work, to you.' She carefully kept her voice neutral. 'So that's why you were so late this evening? You were interviewing a new chef?'

He nodded, putting down the last empty shell. 'And I'm beginning to think the customers have a treat in store.'

'I suppose so.' As quietly as she could, she sighed.

'Damn it——' his quick ear had caught even that tiny whisper of sound '—I've apologised, haven't I?'

'So that's all right, then,' she flashed back.

'I don't know what's got into you tonight...' He wrestled with his quick anger, and mastered it. 'Or maybe I do.'

'You do?' She made it a question, though she was afraid of the answer.

But he only nodded, and reached for her hand across the cloth. 'It's exactly the thing that's made me decide...' He stopped once more.

'Decide what?' she demanded impatiently. '*What* have you decided?'

'Never mind.'

He would say no more, though she went on asking until Étienne brought in the next course. That turned out to be well worth waiting for, and demanded her full attention.

'How on earth did he get it so full of flavour?' she asked, the roast rib of beef melting on her tongue like butter.

'Well, it's Charolais, of course.' Ned always took questions about food preparation seriously. 'And he's left it on the bone. And when it was cooked he'll have let the juices concentrate...'

Rachel listened with a growing sense of the world being a better place than she had imagined. Perhaps Ned was right, and she'd needed food. It was certainly making her feel better.

And after all, she had reason to be cheerful. It had been business, not Claudette, which had kept Ned here so late.

But then—she put down her knife and fork on her empty plate—but then, couldn't he have had time for both?

'Have some more?' Ned offered.

She shook her head, all appetite suddenly vanished. Of course he'd had time for both. He could easily have made love in the castle, and had a beer here afterwards. He might even have been glad of the chance to hire Étienne, as a cover for what he'd really been doing...

No, that at least didn't ring true. Ned would never use business to cover anything. He took it too seriously for that.

'Perhaps I will, after all,' Rachel said.

She ate a second helping as big as her first. By the time she had finished it, her optimism was so strong she could even speak to test it.

'Couldn't you have got a taxi back? So as not to have kept me waiting so long?'

If only he had! If only he'd come back just an hour earlier, and joined her at the hotel! If he'd done that, she'd never have waylaid Claudette, never have had her mind filled with poison ideas of *cinq-à-sept* ...

'There's only one taxi in St-Jean,' Ned reminded her, 'and he was busy. That's why I had to walk.'

And of course, walking was exactly what he'd been doing. He'd make nothing of the downhill two miles or so back to town.

'Though to tell the truth, I was glad of the exercise,' he added a little ruefully. 'After sitting still and talking French all afternoon.'

Sitting still and talking French. Not lying down and... Rachel's mind hastily rejected those other things he might have been doing. Maybe, after all, he hadn't done any of them.

'Oh, well,' she murmured, as near to peace as she'd been since she arrived in France. 'It's... it's nice here.' Over the empty silver dishes she reached out her hand, and was glad to have it folded in his. 'Thank you for bringing me here, my darling.'

The pudding turned out to be a marvellous concoction which Étienne called *Poire du Berry*. Rachel gorged happily on its spicy mixture of pears and cognac, pastry and cream, but refused a second helping. Ned, however, took a spoonful more, and tasted it with careful calculation.

'I wonder how it would freeze for our gourmet food range?'

'Can't you forget about business for a minute?' Rachel smiled at Étienne as he cleared the plates, then yielded to an engulfing sleepiness and closed her eyes. 'When's the taxi coming...? Heavens, more to eat?' She stared down at the wooden cheeseboard Étienne had left for them. 'I couldn't.'

'Not even a little Tour des Chats?' Ned cut the tiniest wedge of a cheese she didn't recognise, a white disc with a risen top like a cake. 'Remember, this is its best season.'

She tasted it reluctantly, not wanting to like it. 'It's certainly very... fresh,' she decided, charmed in spite of herself by its creamy softness. 'It tastes of...' she held out her plate for more '...of meadows in spring.'

'Exactly.' He rewarded her with a slightly bigger piece, and refilled their glasses with the cooled white wine Étienne had left with it. 'I'm glad you had the chance to try some on the spot.'

She watched him cut a handsome section of the same cheese for himself. 'I don't know where you put all you eat.'

'There's always the odd corner.' He tranquilly buttered the crackling end of the bread to go with his cheese. 'Besides, we didn't have so very much. A bit of shellfish, a bit of asparagus...' The blue eyes lengthened in gentle mockery. 'You're always on about seafood and vegetables being good for me.'

'It wasn't seafood, and there was all that hollandaise——' she swung automatically into their old, half-serious argument '—and that beef would be brimming with cholesterol.'

'We have to eat.'

'And you certainly do...'

She trailed off, not wanting to nag. After all, he'd never shown the least sign of heart trouble; it was only that she worried in case he might. At home, she dealt with her worry by keeping them on as healthy a diet as possible, but she sometimes wondered why she bothered. Whatever he did and whatever he ate, he stayed impossibly fit.

'And you never even gain any weight,' she added, sighing. 'It's not fair.'

'I burn it all up as energy,' he announced smugly. 'As I will tonight...'

He broke off and closed his mouth tight, the violet-shadowed eyes suddenly watchful. A new chill ran down Rachel's spine, a cold suspicion which banished her new-found content like a wintry wind. She sat straight in her

chair, and faced him with all the courage which the good
food had put into her.

'And how will you do that?'

He relaxed, smiled, and ate the last of his cheese.
Clearly he had no intention whatever of answering her.

Well, this time he wouldn't get away with it. This time,
she decided, he was going to tell her the truth.

'How,' she persisted with the cold logic of despair,
'will you manage to be so energetic, at this time of night?
It's——' she glanced at the clock on the wall opposite,
its cruel edged pendulum swinging back and forth in the
glass-fronted walnut case '—quarter to twelve. Have you
by any chance——' she threw caution to the winds
'—got a midnight date?'

'As a matter of fact, yes.' He laid his damask napkin
by his empty plate. 'I suppose it's about time you knew.'

'Knew what?' She felt as if she were rushing towards
the edge of a cliff, but she wouldn't stop now. 'What've
you been hiding from me?'

He sat for another minute, the violet-shadowed gaze
moving over her. Slowly and with every sign of enjoyment he took in her forehead and cheeks where the
uncombed hair fell over them, her mouth, the round
neck of her T-shirt. When he reached the swell of her
breasts his eyes lingered, then shuttered off as he rose
to his feet and held out a commanding hand.

For a moment, Rachel stared almost with hatred at
that arrogantly confident hand. Then, without her will,
she put hers into it, and rose beside him.

'Here we go, then,' he said, mysteriously cheerful.

'Where to? Has the taxi come?'

He started them toward the door. 'Forget about the
taxi.'

'What?' She dug her heels in, refusing to go along with him any further. 'You aren't seriously intending to walk after all? So that's what you meant about exercise ...'

'That's not what I meant about exercise.' He gave up trying to pull her, and instead turned for another of those lingering, enjoying inspections. '*This* is what I meant about exercise.'

His hands closed on her waist, drawing her to him whether she would or not. Would she, would she not? She didn't know—perhaps she never would. Perhaps she would never know anything ever again but the agonising pleasure, the inflaming satisfaction of his mouth on hers.

His hands slid from her waist to her back, and on down, pressing her close to him. Against her belly, through all the layers of her clothes and his, she felt the beloved weapon which had so often wounded her, so often made her whole. He could make her want that wounding, that wholeness, more than anything else in the world, but he mustn't do it now, not now...

'Not now.' His lips moved against hers like an answer to her roiling, unspoken thoughts, and he dragged his mouth away. 'Have you gathered,' he almost whispered, 'that we aren't going back to town?'

'So where *are* we going?' Exasperation helped her master herself, and the real world rushed back to her with all its bitterness. 'I'm told there's a bed of moss in the castle...'

She trailed off, wishing she'd bitten her tongue before it could form the words. And of course he was pretending not to know what she meant—what else could he do?

'What are you on about, Jel?' He laid his strong, cool fingers on her forehead. 'You're all right, are you? You didn't hit your head——?'

'Of course I'm all right.' She jerked irritably clear. 'Just wanting some sleep. I suppose you've persuaded them to make us a pair of shakedowns here, then?'

'Shakedowns,' he repeated, for some obscure reason of his own pleased with the idea. 'You could call it that. Come and see.'

He commanded her hand again and, as before, she had to let him take it. He tucked it into the crook of his arm as if he were an eighteenth-century beau and, thus in control, walked her out of the restaurant. Along the corridor they went, through another massive double door, up the shallow stone steps of a wide staircase, and along another corridor.

'Apples?' Rachel snuffed up the scent as they trod an endless strip of dark carpet over wide, ancient oak floorboards. 'Do they store fruit up here?'

'Sh!'

She jumped as a board creaked under her feet. 'Can't we have more light?' She cowered close to him in the apple-scented dimness.

'There's light enough.'

And there was—a pearly stream of it—from yet another double door which stood open to receive them.

CHAPTER SEVEN

'WHAT on earth...?' Rachel stood on the threshold with her mouth open. 'Who...? How could...?' She stopped, and tried again. 'This *is* a country inn, isn't it?'

'Exactly.' Delighted with his surprise and with her re-action to it, Ned urged her forward. 'That's just how it took me, when I first saw it. A room like this, in a country inn?'

She stepped cautiously into it with him, half expecting the whole luscious mirage to disappear. But no, their feet really did touch first shining parquet then deep, glimmering carpet as pale as dawn-misted water.

'Water.' She dropped her hand from his arm and went ahead of him to that grand, fantastic, dominating bed. 'That's the whole theme, isn't it?'

From where she stood, the bedhead was hidden in drifts of lace. She hardly looked at it, so intent was she on the two alabaster swans which rose life-size and magnificent from the foot. Each had one translucent wing raised; each superb neck curved out into the room.

'What is it about them?' She stroked one minutely carved, real-seeming, strangely curving neck. 'I mean, why make them all sort of sideways like this? They're so true to life otherwise.'

'They're still true to life.'

She studied the carved beaks where they drooped over the misty-water carpet. 'I've never seen swans turning their necks in that funny way.'

'I have.' He sauntered up to join her.

'When they're hurt? How sad, to show them like that...'

'They're...' the deep voice broke a little, strangely out of control '...they're not hurt.'

She jerked round to face him. 'Why are you laughing at me?'

He shook his head, refusing to tell. Yet clearly he *was* laughing, though the blue eyes had half closed and the long mouth pressed tight to keep it in.

'Have another look,' he urged, 'and work it out yourself.'

Irritated, she turned back to the two swans. Certainly those sideways-drooping necks didn't convey hurt or sadness. In fact, the sculptor had made each round bird eye a little longer than it should be, and tilted each beak to an almost human air of...satisfaction? Complacence? No, it was more than that—almost the bird faces showed a sly delight, as if more pleased about something or other than they cared to admit.

'Maybe this other one,' he suggested, strolling to the head of the bed, 'can help you work it out.'

'What?' She looked up from the riddle he was so enjoying. 'What other one?'

He stood by one of the gilded night tables. His great figure blotting out the light from its mother-of-pearl lamp, he raised a strong-outlined arm to the bedhead, and she saw that the draped lace half concealed a third swan.

'Oh!' She took in the rearing male arrogance of this other bird, and to her astonishment felt herself blushing. 'But that's...it's...'

He nodded, laughter spilling from the blue eyes at last. 'Got it in one.'

'But...but that means you have to sleep between them when they're just about to...'

'That's the idea.'

'How...how perfectly indecent!'

'Which is exactly how you're meant to feel when you see it. Funny, that.' He dropped into the padded pale velvet of a shell-shaped chair, his long legs dark-suited across the dawn-water carpet. 'You wouldn't think it'd still work, after ninety-odd years. But it does, doesn't it?'

'Ninety years,' she repeated, her mind skating away from the rest of what he was saying. 'Is that how old it is?'

'Come here.' He stretched out an arm, the rolled-up sleeve glimmering white, the forearm golden and formidable in the pearly light. 'Let me tell you about it.'

'No!' She was surprised at her own sharpness, and wondered if he could hear the quavery undertone. 'I mean, I'm curious of course, but...but...'

She trailed to helpless silence. How to convey her unease at the sight of him, her own great, arrogant male, so much at home before that extraordinary bed? It wasn't that he looked as if he belonged here—no man could belong in such a room. Much worse, he looked as if he *owned* the place. As if he'd had it created purely for his pleasure.

She let her eyes wander over the male angles of him in that absurd shell chair. His shoulders were too wide for it, but it lovingly cradled the lower part of his body—the flat waist and narrow hips and the tops of the long, concealed thighs...

She turned away. 'I...I just don't feel I know you at all,' she told him. 'Everything's been strange all day, but now...' She cast round for a way of explaining, and caught sight of an enamelled, swan-wreathed clock on a shell-carved chest of drawers ' . . . now, it's as if *you'd* become a complete stranger,' she finished, shrinking a little from the truth of it. 'As if you'd turned into a stranger at midnight.'

She felt herself tense as she waited for his reply. Would he dismiss what she had just said as nonsense—mere feminine whimsy not to be taken seriously? If he did that, something would die in her. She'd go on loving him—she couldn't help that—but she'd never again look to him for the special understanding she was asking of him now.

'It's all me, Jel.' He wasn't brisk and dismissive, but he wasn't understanding either. 'Whatever you're seeing at this moment, it's always been there.' He gestured again with that formidable arm. 'Why don't you come and sit on my lap, and try and tell me more?'

'No! Please!' She found she was shivering. 'Just don't touch me for a while, all right?'

He shrugged, and she looked for somewhere else to sit. That stool would do—velvet-padded before a dressing-table gilded like the two night tables with sinuous water-lilies. She took it and faced him, straight backed, hands rigidly controlled on her lap.

'Now, then.' She was pleased to hear her own voice coming out so strongly. 'Tell me about this incredible room.'

'Well . . .' He paused, smiled at her impatient gesture, and indulged it. 'You've heard of *les Grandes Horizontales*?'

'The grand horizontals?' she translated, puzzled. 'Sounds like geometry.'

'Biology, more like.' Laughter spilt once more into the deep tones. 'And history, I suppose. At the turn of the century, this inn was owned by one of them.'

'They were people then, these . . . horizontals?' She repeated the unlikely word in bewilderment.

'Weren't they just. This one retired here for a quiet life, after she'd had enough of the city.'

'It was a woman?'

'Had to be. And naturally she brought all her gear, including this——' his muscular arm swept out to indicate the bed and all the furniture '—which had been a present from her most faithful . . . admirer.'

'So, though a woman owned all this,' she put in slowly, working it out, 'it was a man who paid for it?'

'I told you, she was one of *les Grandes Horizontales* . . .' He broke off, remembering that he hadn't explained the term. 'That was the nickname in those days for the famous Paris courtesans.'

'I see.'

And Rachel did see. After what he'd told her, even the half-open petals of the gilded water-lilies, languorous and yearning, roused images in her mind which she didn't want to think about. Shutting them out, she glanced round. The pale walls were neutral as the carpet, but what about that life-size painting of a naked girl provocatively entangled with a swan? What about those bedside lamps, each light rearing from a half-open, mother-of-pearl oyster?

'So this place,' she began with distaste, 'is a relic of some . . . some kept woman?'

'She'd be a bit more than that,' he corrected mildly. 'They were one of the sights of Paris, the *Horizontales*. Royals and millionaires danced to their tune.' The bright head turned to her, trying to make her share his interest. 'This one was called the swan, because of——'

'I don't want to know.'

'What's the matter with you?' He drew his legs up and sat forward, vigorous hands on high-angled knees. 'This room's amazing, but it's still history. Why get so worked up about it?'

'I don't know.' She closed her eyes, and shook her head to clear it. 'You've sprung so many surprises on me this evening that I don't know where I am any more.'

'Oh, well, if that's all . . .'

He stood up, and crossed the pale carpet to tower over her. She flinched away, but when he took her two hands she had to give them, and when he drew her upright she had to rise, weak and unsteady though she was.

'Let me help you work out where you are.' The deep tones caressed the air by her temple. 'You're in a room made for . . .'

He broke off, a breath apart from her, hands warm round hers. In the pearl-white light of the oyster lamps, she could see that his eyes had lost all those violet over-tones which had so confused her in the restaurant. Now they glinted their usual steel-blue, the eyes of a man who knew what he wanted and how to get it. She looked away, evading their clear message.

'Made,' he continued, 'for what we were starting to do just before we came up here. Remember?'

'I'm hardly likely to forget, seeing . . .' she studied the neutral wallpaper above his shoulder ' . . . seeing it's for-bidden until . . . until we've sorted ourselves out.'

'It isn't forbidden any more.'

'What?' She jerked round to stare up at him.

'As far as I'm concerned, we're sorted.' He lifted her hand to his lips. 'Now all we have to do is enjoy ourselves. And I do intend to enjoy myself...' He paused, conscious of her resisting palm straining back and refusing his kisses. 'What's the matter?'

'What brought this on?' She tried to pull her fingers free.

'Lots of things.' Instead of letting go, he pinned her hands behind her back. 'I'll tell you all about it some time.'

Now it was her whole body which strained away from him. 'Tell me about it *now*.'

'Certainly not. I've better things to do.'

And he began to do them. First his lips closed on her earlobe, nibbling and tasting; then they started a devastating track over her reluctant, turned-away cheek. She shivered, and tried once more to free her hands. Beyond him she could see those wretched, complaisant female swans, carved no doubt by some man...

'And he didn't even get it right, for all the fuss to be realistic,' she burst out as Ned's dangerous mouth approached hers. 'Swans go in twos, not threes.'

'What are you on about now?'

He had lifted his lips from the corner of hers, to stare down at her. Glad of the relief, she indicated the bed.

'Whoever made that thing got it wrong. Cobs...' She hesitated, a little self-conscious over the word he had taught her for a male swan, then swept on with renewed indignation. 'Cobs don't have harems, they have one wife. One pen——' she gave the female, too, its right name '—for life.'

'So what?' He shrugged, not really interested. 'It's only to fit the bed, so the pens can each raise a wing over it.'

'Then why aren't there two cobs? Why haven't the pens a mate each? I'll tell you why,' she persisted, holding him off with words. 'It's because the...the man who paid for this room meant himself to be the only male in it.'

'Rubbish.' He took up her argument in his usual downright manner. 'There's the cob, isn't there?'

'But don't you see? That's *him*,' she shot back in triumph. 'That's how he saw himself, the man who bought all this. That's why he only had one male swan——' she glanced towards the bedhead with distaste '—lording over two females like real swans never would. This place,' she rushed on, determined to finish her argument, 'is a male sexual fantasy made real.'

'And that's wrong?' The steel-blue eyes snapped with the beginnings of irritation. 'Of all times to get feminist——'

'Look at those lamps,' she cut in feverishly, not knowing what she hoped for. 'Go on, have a really good look at them, and see what they make you think of.'

He turned at her insistence, and at once she knew why she had asked him to. The minute his attention was elsewhere, she shook off his loosened grip and dashed to the door. She would have been out and fleeing down the corridor, but for the painted china doorknob, which simply wouldn't turn however hard she wrenched...

'What's got into you?' He came after her, pushing between her and the still-shut door. 'Do you want to wake the whole inn?'

'*Somebody* must be awake,' she half sobbed. 'They must be, to let me out.'

'Let you out to what?' He caught her dodging waist with ease and held it, his voice purposefully low and soothing. 'Where d'you think you can go, at this time of night?'

'Isn't there a taxi coming some time? You rang for one...' She glared at him with new suspicion. 'Didn't you?'

'I only made one call,' he admitted coolly, 'to tell Madame Robert we wouldn't be back tonight.'

'What?' She broke away from him and edged backwards, driven in spite of herself into the depths of that depraved, unnatural, fascinating room. 'You did that? Without a word to me?'

'It was supposed——' the deep voice was only mildly regretful, even a little amused '—to be a surprise.'

'You didn't honestly think I'd *like* this place, did you?'

'Why not? That bed's a local show-piece. Honeymooners beg to be allowed to sleep in it.'

'Honeymooners!' she repeated, ever more outraged. 'To think of a bride, in that...' She choked to a halt, but not for long. 'Everything here's been...made by men for their own pleasure...why, that's it!' She faced him at last as the clue fell into place. 'That's why I felt you were a stranger just now.'

'A stranger.' He considered the idea for a moment. 'Right, then.' He fixed her with that glinting blue gaze. 'You're about to make love with a stranger.'

'I'm not! I won't!' She shook her head so violently that her hair flew out round her shoulders. 'You've taken this room for your own pleasure——'

'And yours, Jel. When I asked Madame Lebrun before dinner if we could spend the night here——' the blue eyes held hers '—I was thinking of...well, lots of things, but all to do with you.'

'Were you?' She swallowed, for here was the heart of it. 'Were you really thinking of me. Only me? Not...'

Not Claudette Grenier, she might have gone on, if her tongue could have formed the words. If her voice could have obeyed her, and not refused to leave her throat. She dragged in another uneven breath, and tried not to think of that other bed within the walls of the castle, that couch of moss in the afternoon sun...

'Who else would there be to think of?' he demanded with perfect self-possession. 'You're my girl, aren't you?'

She saw her chance at last. 'Your *only* girl?'

'So that's what this is all about.' He stared at her with new understanding. 'You're still letting Claudette bug you. Thank heaven for that.'

'What?' She jerked up again to meet his eyes. 'What's so good about it?'

'Nothing, but it does explain why you've been carrying on like this. Now stop playing up, love.' He advanced on her, so overwhelmingly male that he seemed suddenly to become the very force and focus of this female room. 'Forget silly adolescents who don't matter, and come to Ned.'

'Keep away from me!' She fell back before him. 'You're no better than...' she waved her arms about her, stuck for words '...than all the others who paid for this...this horizontal swan...' She broke off, furious with herself for being so muddled. 'Stop laughing at me!'

'Why?' But he straightened his mouth, and brought himself to order. 'I like laughing at you. It's part of loving you.'

'It's part of not taking me seriously as a person.'

'Now that's where you're wrong.' He came on towards her, driving her before him over the dawn-water carpet. 'I do take you seriously as a person. Very seriously indeed.'

'You don't, you don't!' She staggered backwards, and felt the monstrous bed loom ever nearer. 'I don't believe you've ever taken any woman seriously in all your life.'

'You may be right there.' His gaze swept down over her curves, rose to her face, and settled on her mouth. 'Mention it again some time, and we'll talk about it.'

'Don't touch me...'

But she might as well have told the sun not to rise, the river not to flow. Already he was on her, above and about and around her, circling her with his arms while his mouth came down on hers. Already her body was opening to him as her lips had opened, to let him rise and flow wherever he pleased.

'No,' she pleaded weakly as he raised the hem of her robin-red T-shirt. 'No...'

He didn't answer, just went on raising it. Up it came and she was actually helping him, holding her arms above her head so that he could slide it off and away. For a moment she stayed like that, arms curved round her head and eyes tight shut, not daring to look down at her own naked breasts. Then she felt his hands, dream-light on either side of her waist, and her eyes flew open.

'Why so gentle? You're not usually so gentle.'

'Anybody would think——' the blue eyes lengthened in amusement '—that I usually knock you about.'

'No, but...'

She trailed off, shuddering. His lips brushed each of her shoulders in turn, touched the hollow at the base of her throat, and moved on. Then he sank to his knees before her in a quick, silent movement which left a rush of cool air fanning her skin. She stared down at the bright, curving hair, the wide shoulders, the strong arms which in their rolled-up sleeves still held her on either side, and wondered why she so much didn't want all this.

He was claiming her breasts now, his lips on one throbbing tip. She let out an unwilling gasp, pleading for she knew not what, but already he had moved to the other. She buried her fingers in his hair, trying to make him do what she wanted, but he wouldn't. That breast, like the other, was allowed only a quick, tantalising salute, and his lips moved on.

'You're so...so different,' she complained, her fingertips tracing the warm, deceptively familiar lines of his head. 'Why have you changed so?'

'I've told you why.' His voice came up low and muffled from her midriff, which he was kissing in its turn. 'This is a new start, for both of us.'

'But why do we need a——?'

'Quiet, Jel. Just let me love you.'

As if she could ever have stopped him. And yet, far away in the depths of her memory, a tiny voice echoed.

''e kiss my shoulders,' Claudette had said, 'then my throat, then my lips. Then 'e take the flowers of my breasts, gently, so gently...'

Was that why he spoke of a new start? Was it because this afternoon, from five till seven, he had learnt a new sensuality, a new treasuring of the female body, from a new, outspoken partner? Rachel made a convulsive movement, trying to free herself of the poisoned caresses, but it was no use. It wasn't only that he wouldn't let her go. Much worse, she didn't even want him to.

'Just let me love you,' he repeated, his lips against her flesh, 'now and forever...'

'No! Not until I've...not until you've...'

She trailed off, helpless. With a skilful flick he had undone the fastening of her jeans, and pushed them down over her hips. She was aware of them sliding away, taking her briefs with them and leaving her achingly unprotected. Hampered by the folds of denim, she could only wait, trembling, while his tongue traced the mark the waistband had left on her skin.

'N-no! P-please...' she gasped, closing her eyes and shuddering. 'It's not right, not now, not here...oh!'

Her eyes flew open. He was standing up, leaving her, becoming a separate being, and she could hardly bear it. But it wasn't for long. Already he was scooping her into his arms, collapsing jeans and all...

To put her on that bed? She wouldn't have it. She'd fight him. She'd get her T-shirt back, walk alone through the forest, anything rather than...

But it was all right: he'd only set her gently on the little shell chair. On his knees before her once more, he pulled off her trainers.

'What beautiful feet.' He lifted one to examine. 'Such a high arch, and then under all this...' he grasped the folds of denim, and drew them off her '...such a narrow ankle. Wonder why I've never noticed?'

And why are you noticing now? she wanted to ask. Where did you learn to notice such things? Were you taught this afternoon, on a bed of moss...?

She couldn't say it. If she did, he might stop kissing her ankle, and the arch of her foot, and each of the toes in turn. Wasn't it worth a little silence to have this god-like stranger kneeling before her, bowing his bright head over her foot, touching it again and again with his lips? She clenched herself together, lest her pleasure spill over and wash away the world.

It had never been like this before. Never until now. This wasn't her practical, everyday Ned whose touch had become so familiar. This was a demon lover, a man possessed...

But possessed by whom? Whose lover had he been? Who had made this happen to him?

'Don't!' She pushed him away and sprang out of the shell chair, naked and defenceless though he had made her. 'I don't want this...' She had to stop there, and shut her eyes tight, and bury her hands in the curving softness of his hair.

He hadn't even needed to rise to his feet. A half-turn, and the white-sleeved arms had easily caught her, and drawn her once more within their imprisoning circle. They closed round her, and the sweet, relentless mouth circled her belly with a trail of quick, hard kisses. Round and round his lips circled, covering every shrinking, eager, tumultuous inch, slowing as they neared her navel. When they reached it, they paused as at a shrine.

'You...' Her voice came out small and breathless, but she had to say it. 'You never did this before...'

'No more talk, my darling.'

The words were muffled against her flesh. Still he knelt before her, his mouth moving on down, down... Rachel closed her eyes and clung to him, defeated by her own womanhood.

'No...'

That was what she meant to say, but all she managed was a wordless, yearning gasp. He didn't have to hold her now; it was she who held him, lost to all reason, lost to everything but the hot springs of pleasure he was releasing in her. It had never been like this, it couldn't be like this; never in all the world was such joy ever possible...

And yet he had more for her. His hands, freed from their task of holding her, rose to her breasts, and his fingers started a complex dance on each coral-hard peak. She shuddered and swayed, a primitive creature swimming in a sea of pleasure.

He let out a muffled, throaty exclamation as the soft weight of her breasts fell forward against his fingers. She was leaning down to him, offering herself wholly, her own hands reaching out blindly towards this stranger who had made her want him so much. She sighed with satisfaction as she found the rippling shoulders beneath their light covering.

'Please,' she whispered, surfacing for a moment. 'I want to touch you.'

Slowly, reluctantly, he drew his hands and his lips from her body. Slowly, reluctantly, he rose to his feet and stood facing her. She stared up at him, loving the gleaming hair that fell over the high forehead, the intent, compelling eyes, the strong nose, the long mouth full and moist with desire. Her glance moved on to the square chin, the bronzed column of his neck, the broad, tanned chest emerging as he tore at the buttons of his shirt...

'No.' She put a hand up to stop him. 'Let me.'

The last button undone, she pushed it away and down, not caring where it fell. What she cared about was here under her hands. The warm span of his shoulders rippled with life, the perfectly developed chest rose and fell under its sprinkling of fine gold hair, the heart beat fiercely in the powerful rib-cage. Further down, the hard belly was circled and half hidden by the dark worsted band of his trousers, but she could soon fix that. She set her hands to the fastening.

'Are you ready for me, my darling?'

'What do you think?' And he laughed—an exulting, masculine sound which cut like a sword through this feminine room...

This room which had seen so much of male desire and of female compliance. Where he had brought her without her consent, where he had become a stranger who made love to her whether she would or not. She turned from him, instinctively huddling her arms over her straining, tell-tale breasts.

'Now what?' The soft burr of a zip, the soft scuff of falling cloth, a light step, and he was before her. 'Are you maybe still hoping you'll get away from me?'

She looked helplessly at his magnificent nakedness. What could she do against such vibrant, animal power? Her lowered glance took in the broad, tanned chest, and moved on in spite of all her efforts to stop it. She tried to halt it at the flat belly, but it wouldn't be halted. She had to look further, to seek the fine line of hair which gradually widened to a springing triangle, a gilded frame for the loved, dreaded weapon... It was almost a relief when he swung her up into his arms.

'Because you won't ever escape me now,' his breath warmed her ear. 'Not ever.'

'No.' She leant against him in despair, in love, in longing.

'From now on,' he exulted, his cheek caressing her hair as he carried her over the pale carpet, 'there's always going to be us. You, me and the children.'

'Ch-children,' she repeated stupidly, too drugged with sensuality to take in the meaning.

'A boy for me, a girl for you.' He lowered her and set her on something soft, a blue-green counterpane printed with swirling wave patterns. 'Which do you hope for first, my darling?'

'What? Oh. I don't know.' She drew a shuddering breath, her impatience barely contained. 'B-both.'

'Twins?' His laugh now was open and exulting as he leant over her. 'What shall we call them?' He sat by her on the bed, his flank warm against hers, tormenting himself as well as her with this deliberate delay. 'What about Castor and Pollux?'

'I...I don't know.' She met the steely, victorious eyes in a fury of frustration. 'Who are Castor and Pollux?'

'The twins in the zodiac.' He lifted a powerful, naked arm to something behind and over her head. 'Swan princes...'

'*Swan* princes?'

She strained her head backwards to see up to where he was pointing. And there it was: that shameless, carved cob swan, rearing in male pride over two pens together in a way no real swan would ever do. Only a man would do that—have one woman for the afternoon, and another for the night. One to enjoy, the other to bear his children...

'All right.' She raised herself on one elbow. 'All right, I'll bear your children.'

He snapped to attention, alert to her change of mood. 'Now what's got into you?'

'I can't help loving you, and you know it.' She let the words flow out of her, calm with the strength of her new resolve. 'You know you can do what you like with me——'

'Ha!' It was a short, ironic bark of disagreement.

'You can,' she insisted. 'You've made me want you, and you've brought me to this bed, though you know I hate it...' she held up a hand to silence his interruption '...and now you're going to...' she paused, teasing out the central idea from the confusion of her feelings '...to have the new start you talked about. But it'll be a bad start for me.' She sought his eyes. 'I may never forgive you for it.'

Once more, as when she had tried to explain his strangeness, she tensed for his reply. Would he understand? Would he even try to understand? He wanted her as urgently as ever, she could see that. Would he yield to that urgency, rekindle her own need as he so easily could, sweep her feelings aside as he'd done till now, and take his uncomplicated male pleasure with her? Or would he listen to her at last?

His face grown rock-hard and unreadable, he put a light hand on her breast. She sank back on the pillows in despair as her treacherous body leapt to his palm, and the hot springs of pleasure gushed anew within her.

Maybe I'm asking too much, she thought. Let it go, she told herself, and waited for the flawed joy which would be hers when he claimed and mastered her.

It didn't happen. Instead, his hand slowly dropped away, his fingers leaving a fiery trail that almost made her moan aloud. She turned impatiently, and found the steel-blue eyes sombre.

'Just testing, Jel.'

'You didn't need to.' Her own voice sounded thick and slurred in her ears. 'I told you, I'm as ready as you are...'

'You really feel so strongly about this bed?'

She closed her eyes so as not to have to see how superbly ready he was, and nodded. 'I hate it.'

'But you'd still...accept me in it,' the deep voice persisted beyond her closed eyes, 'if I made you?'

'You know I would.'

'I suppose I do. Yes,' he repeated slowly, 'I suppose I do.'

She felt a lock of her dark hair move on the pillow. She opened her eyes to find he had raised it and wrapped it round his finger. When he found her watching him he dropped it quickly, and spoke again in a voice brisk as cold water.

'Would you feel able just to—er—*sleep* in the bed? Alone,' he added, standing up, 'while I doss down here on the carpet?'

'I'd never ask you to do that!' She sat up, shocked. 'There's plenty of room in here for two.'

'And you think we'd stay two, once I got in there with you?' Amusement and irritation glinted together in the steel-blue eyes. 'I still want you, Jel.'

'I c-can see that,' she admitted, looking hastily away.

'So up you come——' he took her hands in a new, gingerly grip, and drew her from the bed '—and let's have a blanket.'

Weak with astonishment, she did as he bid her, and stood up. He dropped her hands at once, and started stripping the blue-green counterpane from the bed.

He'd listened to her! He'd taken notice of her feelings, and wasn't going to make her do anything she didn't want to. As it finally sank in, Rachel felt all her worries washed away in a great tide of love for him.

'Oh, my darling!' She opened her arms to him. 'Do put that blanket down, and hold me.'

'Certainly not.' He straightened with his arms full of sea-green blanket. 'You can't have it both ways, Jel. You've fought me off, and now I stay off.'

'You...you do still want me?' she asked, her gaze dropping anxiously to the concealing folds of blanket.

He almost flung them to the floor, and straightened to face her. 'Satisfied?'

'Well, no...'

As far as she knew, she only took one step towards him. Perhaps, she thought as his arms closed round her, perhaps one step was all it needed. She didn't know, because time and space had somehow changed out of all recognition. The whole world was here, between and round them, closing them in and opening them out to a new—an entirely new—joy.

'So you won't have the bed,' he observed when the first transport of it was over, 'but you don't mind the carpet?'

'It's a gorgeous carpet,' she told him dreamily as she snuggled against him. 'Ideal . . . why, Ned!' She drew back, shocked. 'Not already!'

'You did say you wanted twins,' he reminded her.

'No, I didn't really mean it . . . but after all——' she moved against him with a sigh '—after all, why not?'

CHAPTER EIGHT

'HMM? NED?' Rachel put out a sleep-drugged hand, and blindly felt the empty place next to her. 'Where are you?'

'Sh!' Ned's voice dropped strangely from somewhere miles above. 'I'm still here.'

Her questing fingers met a springy ankle, and she wondered why he was standing on the bed. For that matter, why was the bed itself so very hard?

'Oh, yes,' she mumbled, easing up from her numbed shoulder. 'This is France, isn't it? Anything can happen in France.'

'Absolutely anything,' he murmured in reply, and lifted her into his arms.

She didn't bother to open her eyes. 'Where are we going?'

'Nowhere at all, darling.' His cheek rested warm on her hair, and his heart beat slow and steady under her hand. 'Just go back to sleep.'

'All right.'

And she did. So it wasn't until the next morning that she found out how he'd made her spend the night in that bed.

She woke slowly. For those first few moments, all she wanted to do was rejoice in the new ache of completeness deep within her. It was as if she had been newly filled in some part of her she hadn't known existed. Filled and overflowing and soaked with love for the man beside her, she opened her eyes at last to a weird sea-green light as of sun under water.

It came through two tall, unfamiliar windows. Their rectangles of muted brightness struck dim highlights from a gilt dressing-table, then crossed a pale carpet to light the translucent, minutely carved feathers of a raised, outspread wing...

Before she knew it, Rachel was on her feet and rushing to draw the floor-length sea-green curtains. The windows proved to be casement doors, giving out to a narrow balcony which overlooked the broken honey-coloured walls of the castle. Walls which might, or might not, have within them a bed of moss...

'Morning, Jel.' Ned pushed the sheet down on his side of the bed, and sat up against the padded-silk headrest which supported the thrusting cob swan. 'Are you ready for breakfast?'

'Not yet.' She tried to ignore his bronzed, rippling shoulders, the gold-wire tangle of his hair, the rich masculinity of him against the other richness of lace and silk. 'So you made me sleep in that thing after all.'

'Now don't start that again.' He stretched luxuriously, one splendid arm spread above her own dented pillow, the other tangling with the lace hangings. 'I wasn't going to let us spend the night on the floor, with a perfectly good bed available.'

'You could have left *me* on the floor.'

'I could, couldn't I? Just looked after myself and left you to your crazy fancies.' His eyes, a blazing steel-blue in the morning light, flashed open to meet hers. 'Would you really have liked that better?'

'Of course I would. At least,' she added, driven to honesty by that steel-blue gaze, 'I would if you'd stayed there with me.'

'Making two of us acting crazy instead of one.'

'Oh, well.' Defeated by his logic, she shook her hair back over her shoulders. 'At least we didn't make love in it.'

'Not yet.' The long lashes swept down in a suggestive, heavy-lidded stare. 'But if you go on jiggling your breasts at me like that——'

'Don't you dare!' She crossed her arms protectively before her. 'I'd be dressed by now, if I knew where they'd hidden the washbasin.' She looked about her with distaste. 'Have you noticed how this swan's wing——' she nodded to indicate the carved, sunlit feathers '—is cracked?'

'It is ninety-odd years old,' he reminded her serenely. 'And it doesn't show at night, when it matters.'

'It matters all the time...'

But she had to stop, unable to put her thoughts into words. She had opened the curtains with some idea of letting the sun cleanse the decadence from this odious room, but it hadn't worked. Instead, the merciless red-gold of early morning had simply picked out cracked alabaster, flaked gilt, a chip in the mother-of-pearl inlay of the lamp nearest to her. Even the lewd painting had a worn patch, just where the girl's languorous, outflung arm plucked unseeing at a green-stemmed, gold-crowned kingcup...

'It's a handle,' Rachel exclaimed, looking closer at the flower.

'It's a door,' Ned countered with an air of simple common sense. 'Try it.'

She did, and the painting swung towards her on outward-opening hinges. Behind it, a perfectly plain bathroom shone clear and simple as fresh air.

'Madame Lebrun had that put in,' Ned explained, 'where the dressing-room used to be.'

'No gold-dolphin taps?' Rachel scanned the chrome and enamel and porcelain surfaces, each giving back the sunshine with its own innocent gleam. 'No shell-shaped bath? No swans?'

'This is how she chose to have it.'

'Maybe she doesn't like the swans either,' Rachel commented, scenting an ally.

'Maybe.' He yawned. 'She still has the original dressing-room furniture, if you'd like to see it.'

'No, thank you.' Rachel entered the bathroom with relief. 'I wouldn't dream of troubling her.'

In here, life seemed almost normal again. The white enamel bath she presently stood in could have been anywhere. Even its sea-green shower curtains were blessedly ordinary, and soon so was Ned, at the washbasin beyond them, shaving as he did every morning in life.

'How are you managing for a razor?' she called over the welcome, cleansing rush of water.

'Étienne put a throw-away one here for me.'

A throw-away plastic razor—what could be more domestic? Rachel finished her shower in a rush of optimism, which only faded when she found herself back in the swan bedroom with damp hair, no comb, and the castle walls brooding at her through the window.

Had Ned made love to Claudette within those sheltering walls? Scrambling into her jeans and the crumpled robin-red T-shirt, tidying her hair with her fingers, Rachel couldn't stop her mind worrying away at the question. Sometimes it found one answer, sometimes another.

He still hasn't said why he suddenly decided we could start a family, she thought as she stared against her will at those secretive castle walls. Surely *something* must have happened, to make him feel so very different about that?

Could the something be his making love to Claudette? Could he have seen that as a last fling? Maybe the experience had jolted him into new ways of thinking, just as it had taught him new ways of making love ...

'Come in,' Rachel thankfully answered the brisk knock.

It was Étienne who entered, and wished her a courteous good morning. Then he spread a snowy cloth on the inlaid table before one of the windows, and set out bowls of milky coffee, rolls, croissants, butter and jam in silver dishes, and a single, half-open apricot-glowing rose in a silver vase.

'Does *madame* wish anything more?' he asked when it was done.

Only to be really *madame*, Rachel reflected as she thanked him and shook her head. Only to be Mrs Nathan Flavell, for better or for worse ...

But I'm not even sure of that any more, she realised with dismay.

How could she marry Ned, with this worry gnawing at her? Even if he should ask her, which he showed no signs of doing, she didn't know how she would answer.

'Yes, my darling,' she whispered, trying out the words. 'If you'll promise you've really finished with Cl ... with Clau ...'

It was impossible. She couldn't even speak the name; it hurt her throat.

So what would she answer? No, because you've stopped being my Ned? No, because I'll never trust you again? She couldn't say any of those things to him either, she realised as she watched him coming out of the bathroom towelling his hair. Not to the reality of him, shining wet from the shower...

'Can't you ever dry yourself properly?' She took her own towel and scrubbed at his shoulders, loving the sheen of his skin so much that it hurt. 'You ought to catch every cold there is.'

'Steady!' He reached back and twisted the towel out of her grip. 'What's got into you all of a sudden?'

'I don't know.' She flung away from him, and seated herself at the loaded table. 'Maybe I just need some breakfast.'

But she didn't. The little she managed to eat tasted like sawdust. Only the coffee was welcome, a heartening stream of heat and life into her overloaded stomach, her overloaded spirits...

'I see it wasn't breakfast you needed after all,' Ned commented, infuriatingly fresh and brisk in his yesterday's shirt and worse-for-wear trousers. 'So what's wrong?'

'Nothing,' she snapped, and pushed away her half-finished croissant. 'I expect I just ate too much last night. It was far too late for such a heavy meal.'

'Gee, thanks.' He put down his own empty coffee-cup, and squared up to her. 'So much for my bright ideas.'

'What?'

She blinked and sat straighter, aware of a new hardness in him. Sure enough his cheeks had suddenly hollowed, the steely eyes glittering like a newly unsheathed weapon.

'Our special night was ruined because you hated this room.' His mouth had set tight above the suddenly formidable chin. 'Now you tell me dinner was wrong, too.'

'It wasn't, it wasn't!' She almost cried it out, half contrite and half frightened of what she had unleashed.

'I...I ate too much, it was all so delicious...' She trailed off, helpless against this new, chilly power in the man she had believed she knew so well. 'I've never seen you like this before.'

'Maybe you should have. If I'd had any sense——' he thrust aside his own half-eaten roll '—I'd have ignored your vapourings last night, and made love to you where and when I meant to.'

'No!' She shook her head, hating the idea. 'If you had—— '

'You'd have enjoyed it just as much,' he stated unanswerably.

'Perhaps,' she had to agree. 'But afterwards——'

'Afterwards, you'd have blamed me,' he cut in, still the cruel, unanswerable stranger. 'So what's different? What were you doing just now—thanking me?'

'I'm...' She stared down at the damask cloth, a dazzling whiteness between the dark curtains of her hair. 'I'm sorry...'

But even as she spoke, she had to crush down her own rebellious anger. Why should she apologise for not liking something he'd planned without consulting her. She raised her head, determined not to thank him as he was half suggesting she might, yet even so found herself surveying him anxiously.

Was he still angry with her? She couldn't tell. His eyes had hooded now, as if an important part of his mind were already busy elsewhere. For all she knew he was simply bored with what he had called her vapourings, and wanting to think about something more important to him. Yes, he was pushing back his chair with a businesslike flexing of superb muscles.

'Right.' He rose to his feet, his rangy, masculine movements fluttering the feminine draperies around him.

'Let's get on with the next thing, shall we? You wanted me to show you the castle.'

'I *didn't*! I don't know where you get the idea...' She caught his eye, and faltered to silence. 'That,' she managed after a struggle, 'would be very...' she swallowed, and brought it out in a rush '...very nice.'

She wouldn't have dared say anything else. As for asking about beds of moss, or the possible pleasures of *cinq-à-sept*, she trembled at the thought. All she could do was wait while he paid the bill, watch him accept from Madame Lebrun a gothically huge key, and trail after him out of the inn, into the ever brighter sunshine of the courtyard.

'Funny, it all seemed a bit sinister last night,' she found herself gabbling nervously as she hurried to keep up with him. 'The cat door-knocker, for instance... What's this?' She paused at the parked minibus. 'Surely it didn't start life this royal purple?'

But of course it hadn't. Whoever re-sprayed it had also painted an uncountable number of tiny, multi-coloured bubbles flying from a painted champagne bottle on the back. Coloured letters danced drunkenly below the bottle to form the word 'FIZZ', and the whole motif was repeated on the sides.

Rachel peered through the windows at a tangle of wires and boxes. 'It looks like a disc jockey's gear.'

'It is.' Ned drew her to one side as footsteps sounded on the flagstones.

She blinked as Étienne reached them, key poised. He nodded, exchanged a few brisk, incomprehensible words with Ned, let himself into the driving seat of the minibus, and edged it out to the road.

'He's doing a kid's party this afternoon,' Ned told her as the sound of the engine died away into the forest. 'He's gone down to check on power points and things.'

'But...' Rachel searched her memory, wondering what she had missed. 'But I thought he was a cook?'

'He is when the old man lets him. Otherwise he stays busy, one way and another.' Ned took her hand and urged her on with him, past the windows of the restaurant. 'He's got a lot of go in him, that boy. I'm glad I've taken him on.'

'Wait a minute.' She dug her heels in, resisting his speed so that she could turn back to stare at one last, surprising little window. 'That's never a box-office, is it?'

'Of course it is. How else would they take the entrance money?' He paused impatiently. 'I told you last night—people come here in droves.'

'Then where are they now?'

'It's too early yet. That's why I've got this.' He waved the key. 'Anyway, most of the visitors come after dark.'

'Goodness, whatever for?' She recalled the haunted night noises of the forest, and shuddered. 'Aren't they frightened?'

'Of course not, silly.' He strode ahead to the heavy, iron-studded gate, and fitted the huge key into the black ironwork round its solid handle.

'So that's what all the hurry's about.' She joined him at a more leisurely walk. 'You can't wait to work that key.'

Already turning it, he shot her a sideways, smiling glance from under the raised, glinting eyebrows. 'Watch this.'

The lock gave with a noise both weighty and smooth, as of heavy tumblers perfectly oiled, and the gate swung back almost silently.

'Sweet as a nut,' Ned went on with satisfaction. 'The Lebruns certainly look after this place.'

'It's theirs?'

'Didn't I say? It goes with the inn. Let's be moving.' He pinned back the gate with the huge iron hook stapled to the wall of the massive archway. 'We haven't got all day.'

'If the visitors come mostly at night,' Rachel queried, drifting after him, 'why weren't there any last night?'

The only answer was her own voice, echoing back at her from the ancient stones of the gatehouse. Someone had laid a broad wooden walkway here, and Ned was already padding along it with that stride which seemed so indolent, but which yet maddeningly forced her to hurry to keep up.

Clearly, his mind was elsewhere. Was he perhaps recalling the last woman he had known within these walls?

I won't think like that, Rachel told herself. I will not.

She raised her voice to repeat her question. 'I said, where were all the visitors last night?'

'Hmm? Oh.' The sun-gilded head, out on the other side of the entrance, turned back to her at last. 'Sorry, Jel. Nobody was here yesterday because it wasn't one of the evenings.'

'*What* evenings?'

'Come out here, and you'll see.'

'I do wish you wouldn't talk in riddles all the time,' she grumbled as she hurried to obey. 'It wouldn't hurt you to explain now and then... What on earth...?'

She craned her neck to stare, sideways and upwards, at the graded tiers of plastic chairs. Ever higher they rose, on sturdy scaffolding either side of the walkway. Behind the chairs, at the top of this unexpected auditorium, a covered platform held arc lamps, electronic equipment, and a tangle of heavy wiring.

'*Son et lumière*,' Ned explained. 'You know, retelling history with lighting and sound effects. Étienne runs it five times a week.'

She turned to the front, to see where the rows of seats were focused. They all faced a single, ancient wall, three stories high and long enough to have formed one side of a great hall. It seemed strangely light and airy, until she realised that its rows of pillared windows had no frames, no glass, and no rooms behind to be lit by them. Beyond it, birds came and went in the blue morning air. A hen chaffinch hopped from one ground-floor sill to another, followed by its brighter mate, and a young thrush used one of the clerestories as a landing-stage.

'That was built in the fourteenth century.' Ned indicated the wall with one arm in its crumpled, rolled-up sleeve. 'I think it was the Spanish who finally blew it up.'

'And . . . this is all they left?'

'Nearly all.'

Rachel felt suddenly breathless as her eyes ranged over the smooth complexity of that solitary wall. It might be ruined, but it was minutely tended and cared for. No plants had been allowed to settle anywhere in its exposed crevices, and it was surrounded by evenly raked gravel with never a weed in sight.

Of course Claudette was lying! The very idea of a bed of moss being permitted here seemed suddenly ludicrous. Besides, this ruin was on public display, endlessly visited, the last place to be quiet enough for covert love-making. Wasn't it?

'Five evenings a week, you said. And as Étienne was free to cook for us last night——' Rachel summoned all her courage, dreading the conclusion she was reaching '—he couldn't have been running his show. So——' she turned to Ned with her next question '—was the place closed?'

He nodded, and delivered the answer she was seeking like a blow. 'It was closed yesterday from two in the afternoon.'

'So how did you get in? No, don't tell me...' She felt her breath rasping in her throat. '*Madame* gave you the key, as she did just now.'

'Étienne, actually. We got on from the minute we met.'

And neither Madame nor Étienne, Rachel's uncontrollable thoughts continued, need ever know who else had been able to come in. Once he'd pinned back that gate, it must have been child's play to dodge inside. Only it wasn't a child who had entered, but a beautiful, predatory teenager.

'And seeing it was officially closed, you'd have it all to yourselves...'

The words, escaping Rachel like a cry of pain, brought her to her senses. What was she thinking of, to condemn him with no evidence but the word of that same trouble-making teenager?

Luckily, Ned had moved on down the walkway with his back to her, and was too far off to hear her properly. She watched him step off the wooden planks and cross the gravel to that graceful, naked wall, and knew with dreary certainty that he and Claudette, both so perfect, could never have resisted each other. The thought clung like a horse-fly, and would not be dislodged.

'What's that you were saying?' he called over his shoulder, leaning on one of the empty window-sills to survey whatever lay behind it.

'Only about your being all alone here.'

Rachel dragged herself to join him. What was he looking at through that unglazed window—a bed of moss? Was she finally about to see where it had all happened? With a huge effort of will, she set her wayward mind to finding something neutral to add to what she had just said.

'Didn't you find it a bit spooky, here on your own?'

He straightened, and turned to her in amused exasperation. 'Honestly, you girls frighten yourself like kids at Halloween.'

'Us . . . girls?'

'I was thinking of the way Claudette carried on last night.'

'You needn't put me in the same category as her, just because we're both . . .'

Rachel broke off with a gulp, horrified at herself. Luckily, he seemed to have no idea of what she had nearly said.

'Both silly about the dark?' he finished with gentle mockery.

'I *wasn't* silly about it, not the way she was.'

'No.' He was suddenly almost serious. 'You weren't.'

And he stayed facing her, waiting for her to draw near and join him. In the growing dazzle of morning sunlight his hair blazed gold and his eyes silver, almost as bright as that white shirt which so emphasised his wide shoulders and narrow waist. In contrast to the brilliance of his upper half, the long, sober-trousered legs seemed made of darkness. He might have been some supernatural being, half-angel and half-devil. Was it the lying, devil half that made him put up a hand to hide his eyes?

'Is the sun bothering you?' she asked as she reached him. 'It doesn't usually.'

'It is a bit glaring in here. Come on——' he caught up her hand '—there isn't much more.'

Not much more, her mind echoed miserably. Only the place where you let me down, broke faith... She kept her head turned away from the wall, refusing to look through its windows as he drew her along to its far end.

Once there, she had no option. Nothing blocked her view except the low course of another wall, a mere stone or two, which had once joined it at right angles. Rachel could no longer keep from staring over it, though she dreaded what she would see.

What she did see was a maze of more broken walls, below ground level. Flights of steps led down into them, and a great, plain stone fireplace stood oddly complete in their midst.

'Kitchens, cellars, dungeons,' Ned commented at her side. 'As you see, they stood up to the gunpowder better than the rest.'

'Mmm.' She let her gaze wander over the innocent honey-gold stone. 'Is it Étienne who keeps it weeded like this?'

'I suppose so. He's certainly a live wire.'

But she wasn't interested in Étienne and his qualities, only in this desert of broken stones. Not a blade of grass grew anywhere among them, let alone a bed of moss.

'And this is all there is?' she asked, her spirits lifting.

He shrugged. 'A lot of the outer walls survived, but you've seen those. Though there is part of a turret over there.' He nodded into the blue morning beyond the ruined hall. 'That must have had a view once, but the forest's long since covered it.'

'I suppose I'd better look at it anyway.' She turned, skirting the outline of the hall to set off in the direction he had indicated. 'Just to finish the job.'

'Careful.' His light footsteps came after her. 'The ground gets very uneven here.'

'I'm watching.' She stepped round one of the ever more abundant tufts of valerian, already blossoming crimson-pink and scarlet. 'I gather Étienne doesn't weed as far as this?'

'Maybe he just likes the flowers.'

'And this?' She pulled at the ivy cascading down the inside of the tree-shaded wall she had now reached. 'Its flowers are nothing, and it can't be good for the fabric.'

'There's a lot of what you call the fabric——' his dry comment followed her as she turned to the waist-high turret '—and it's lasted a long time...what's the matter?'

'What? Oh.' She found the ivy tendril snapped in her white-knuckled fingers. 'I expect I'm feeling the heat.' She spread her hand wide, taking a bitter pride in its steadiness as the fragment of green stem dropped away from it.

'At nine in the morning? And in this shade?' He glanced up to the foliage which grew as he had described it, almost up to the walls. 'Here, lean on me.'

'No.' She summoned all her strength, and stepped away from his supporting arm towards the quiet bombshell of the turret. 'Er—thank you,' she added, doggedly polite. 'I'm fine. Really.'

And she was, she really was. She could look quite calmly now for the second time into this tiny, sheltered world within the waist-high walls. The sun filtered through the young leaves, dappling the emerald-green

moss with flakes of light so that she couldn't see it
properly...

And now she could. Its cushiony green spread over
the floor of the little tower like a mattress. An early-
morning mattress, not yet sprung back after having been
slept on.

'See how little there's left of it?' Ned's voice sounded
from somewhere far away. 'No view, no loopholes to
spy through or shoot through...'

'It...it still has its uses.' She swung round to face
him, gesturing down at the tell-tale moss. 'Somebody
likes it here.'

'What?' His glance followed the direction of her outflung arm. 'Now who's talking in riddles?'

She didn't respond, only watched his face and waited.
Would the casual interest fade from those blazing blue
eyes? Would the frown clear from the gold-arched brows,
or would it deepen to chagrin as he registered this flattened couch and its message?

If he shows any guilt, I'll leave him, she suddenly re-
solved. I'll get right away from him, here, now, and
forever.

But he was impossible to read. His frown didn't fade,
though the long mouth quirked in a way that could have
meant resignation—at being found out, or merely at
having to cope with more of what he saw as her
vapourings?

'What is all this?' The hooded eyes returned to hers,
giving nothing away. 'So some animal's slept here. So
what?'

'The animal with two backs?' She stiffened her spine,
raised her head, kept her glance on his. 'A man with a
woman?'

He stared at her for a moment more. Then she could almost feel him going from her, his mind shifting to some other level behind the wide forehead. He turned once more to that secret, abandoned couch, so quiet, so perfectly sheltered from the world.

Time stretched. Rachel grew aware of the forest, filled with the hushings and twitterings of unseen creatures. Water gurgled, and a diesel motor moved in the distance along that wild road.

'She told you as well,' he said at last. 'I wonder how many other people she's blabbed to?'

'Does it matter?' Rachel asked, infinitely cold and remote now that she knew the worst.

The vigour of his response made her jump. The gold mane flew about his head as he raised his face in appeal to the burning sky.

'Give me strength! What d'you think'll happen if this——' he indicated the flattened moss '—gets to her father?'

Rachel blinked. 'I suppose he'll be angry——'

'Damn right he will. Angry enough to start throwing his weight about, just when I've got everything nicely tied up.'

'Just when you've...' Rachel floundered to silence, hardly able to believe her ears. 'We're not talking about your deal again, are we? At a time like this?'

'What else would we be talking about? It's what I came here for, isn't it?' He glared down at her, incensed. 'You may be having a holiday, but I'm here on the job——'

'You certainly are,' she retorted, riding the anger that washed through her, 'in every sense.'

'Now what are you on about?'

'As if you didn't know.' She turned away, unable to look at him. 'It must have been very...' she gagged on the word, then spat it out '...very *inconvenient*, my turning up the other night and interrupting you...' She choked to silence as his hand dropped to her shoulder and dragged her round to face him.

'What the hell are you harping back to that for?'

'You're hurting.'

She refused to meet his eyes, but instead put up her own hand and pulled weakly at where his cruel fingers dug into her flesh. His only response was to shake her a little.

'If you aren't the most maddening little cuss...'

He had to stop there, even his resonant tones unable to top the diesel roar on the other side of the wall. The road must be somewhere out there among the trees, she realised distractedly as the car, or whatever it was, went on past them. It changed gear—a muffled thrumming and whining that moved back and forth—then it stopped.

'Thank heaven for that.' Ned released her shoulder, grabbed her wrist, and started back the way they had come.

'Let me go!' She struggled to free herself, pulled along willy-nilly through the wavering valerian. 'What's the hurry all of a sudden? Is it so you don't have to talk?'

'No point in talking when I can't get you to make any sense.' His voice echoed hard edged from the great windowed wall. 'And if you expect to hear from me about what happened back there, you're even sillier than I thought.'

'I'm sillier than *I* thought,' she panted, still his prisoner and having to keep pace with his seven-league strides over the gravel. 'For ever having put up with you at all.'

He thumped on to the wooden walkway and turned to stare down at her. 'What the hell is all this?'

'Don't give me that.' Catching her breath, she straightened and met his eyes. 'At least be honest——'

'Honest!' he exploded, causing the robin on the nearby seat to leap fluttering into the air. 'Of all the idiotic... Listen to me, you little fool.' His voice bit like the edge of a saw. 'I'll tell you as much as you need to know, as soon as I judge you need to know it.'

'You will?' she gasped in fury. 'And when will this mighty judgement take place?'

He didn't answer, only set off thundering along the rest of the walkway. On he swept, dragging her after him between the rows of chairs and through the arching gatehouse.

'I'm used to your arrogance, Ned Flavell,' she managed at last when, one-handed, he had unhooked the gate and clanged it shut behind them, 'but this beats all.' Still held by the wrist, she stood over him while he turned the key in the lock. 'Are you really telling me it's perfectly all right for you to——'

'I'm telling you nothing.' He straightened, released her wrist, and handed her the key. 'Scoot off and give this back to *madame*, will you?'

'Give it yourself!'

But in spite of her defiance she held the key, and let him urge her before him into the inn courtyard. And here stood the vehicle which had made all the noise and given him his excuse to leave the scene of his crime. The one ancient, battered taxi of St-Jean-les-Chats had backed into the yard, and now its driver was leaning comfortably against it, chatting with Madame Lebrun.

'I expect she's catching up with the gossip from town,' Ned murmured as they crossed the yard. 'Well, at least she hasn't heard the choice item about Claudette.'

'How do you know she hasn't?' Rachel hissed.

He had no time to answer, even if he'd meant to. As soon as they saw Ned, the driver and *madame* straightened in respectful greeting. While *madame* smilingly collected the key from Rachel's hand, the driver opened the back door of his cab with deferential speed. Before she knew it, Rachel was in the ancient leathery back seat of the taxi.

What a lot had happened since she first sat here. And not only to herself—she hardly recognised the sleepy, grumbling driver who had so reluctantly brought her from the station a lifetime ago. Normally she would have fumed at the unfairness of this instant respect which Ned could always command and she never could. Today, it hardly seemed to matter.

'Life just *is* unfair,' she observed dismally as he settled beside her and the engine started up. 'If a man wants to sow his wild oats, there isn't a thing to stop him.'

'What about women's wild oats?' he demanded, leaning forward to return *madame*'s wave as the taxi drew out of the gate. 'Wrecking everybody's plans...'

'I really believe that's all you care about.'

'You bet it is.' He relaxed against the worn upholstery, amazingly self-possessed. 'I don't know what's gummed your spark-plugs this time, Jel, but it'll have to wait. I've things to do.'

'But what can you possibly have to do that's more important than...?' She broke off, defeated. 'I just never knew you at all, did I?'

He wasn't even listening. He'd asked the driver something, and the man replied over his shoulder without taking his eyes from the steep, winding road. More questions, more answers, and they eased out of the mountain road to the broad highway, the steeple and roofs of St-Jean already visible. Rachel sat in miserable silence until they stopped before the Hotel du Centre, and the driver at once leapt out to open the door.

'Right.' Ned dropped a swift, hard kiss on her flinching cheek. 'Out you get.'

'What?' She slowly took in the significance of the parting kiss. 'You're going somewhere else?'

'I am, and every minute counts.'

'But...but...'

'Out, Jel.'

And out she went, every nerve in her body screaming protests which her tongue refused to voice. Unspeaking, uncommunicating, she watched the taxi bear him away and, because there seemed nothing else to do, turned to enter the hotel.

At this early hour, the bar was silent and deserted. Their key wasn't on its hook, and she realised for the first time that she'd left their room unlocked all night.

Well, what of it? she thought as she dragged herself up the stairs. What did it matter? What, she demanded of herself as she opened the unlocked door, did anything matter now...? She stood transfixed as a small, feminine yelp greeted her appearance in the open doorway.

'You frighten me,' Claudette complained as if she had a right to be here. 'I come to return this.' She held out some dark garment.

It was a formal jacket. Ned's jacket, Rachel recognised with sick dismay. This was the other half of the suit he'd started the day in yesterday. He'd said it was in the Grenier car, but that hadn't been true. It was Claudette who had told the truth after all, and here was the proof, the dark worsted material wildly crumpled as if it had been slept in.

Or rather, slept *on*, Rachel amended to herself. But no, that wasn't right either. They weren't sleeping...

In a black haze of misery, she watched Claudette's long coral-pink nails clutching the battered garment. Incredibly, as if it mattered, the girl was shaking it out as any good housewife might. A shower of woodland debris fell from it: a twig, a dead leaf, the faded scarlet of a broken valerian, and endless, brilliant, snapped-off fragments of poison-green moss.

CHAPTER NINE

'GET out.' Rachel startled herself with her own harshness, each word bitten off with white-hot precision. 'And take that thing with you.'

'But 'e need it,' Claudette half whispered, grey-green eyes wide, pink lips parted as if in fright. ''e must wear it this afternoon, for 'is appointment with Maître Gérard...'

Her breathy little squeak faded into the unreceptive air. In her brown pleated dress with the high, modest collar, dark gold hair smooth under a figured brown band, she seemed a mere child. A good little girl caught out in some naughtiness, she held up the battered jacket.

'There is time for me to sponge and press it like new. I know 'ow; *Maman* make me learn.'

Rachel frowned, surprised by this new angle on the home life of the Greniers. Did Madame Grenier really teach her adored and petted daughter how to valet men's clothes?

'She say all good wives must know zis,' Claudette added, 'and zough I do not wish to marry I am glad now to 'ave learnt it.'

'So why didn't you fix the jacket at home? But no——' Rachel saw how foolish the question was '—you can't have your family recognising it, can you, and guessing what you've been up to?'

'Last night, I crash my car into Papa's new Citroën,' the girl admitted with bowed head. 'Now 'e take mine away. If I am any more bad, 'e say, I do not go to the Sorbonne.'

'I'm glad to hear it. You're not fit...'

Rachel trailed off with a sigh. Why wasn't she taking more pleasure in the sight of this little schemer so chastened and cast down? But she just couldn't. Seeing the jacket clutched to that slender midriff as if for protection, she almost wanted to offer words of comfort. She certainly wouldn't add another scolding to the many Claudette had clearly already suffered.

'Do what you like.' Suddenly immensely tired, she took her empty suitcase from its place against the wall. 'But if you want an iron you'll have to ask Madame Robert.'

'You will do that for me?' The yellow head tilted pleadingly. 'Madame Robert, I do not think she like me much.'

Rachel set the opened suitcase on the bed, and moved about the room gathering her things together. 'Now why on earth should anyone not like you?'

'The people of this town, they are so narrow,' Claudette explained earnestly, the sarcasm lost on her. 'So small, so without vision.' She waved the abused jacket. 'Maître Gérard, for example, 'e will not pardon Ned to come to 'is appointment so...' She broke off with sudden resolution. 'I will fetch the iron myself. I would not wish Ned to lose 'is mill.'

'His what?' Rachel looked up from the dressing-table, the brush and comb suspended in her hands.

'Maître Gérard's grandfather, 'e was the last miller,' the girl explained. 'It mean much to 'im, this water-mill by the forest, although it no longer make flour——'

'By the forest?' Rachel recalled the tumbledown building and rusting machinery she had discovered on her walk the day before. 'You don't mean the ruined one just above the town?'

'Ned will rebuild. That is why Maître Gérard interests himself—'e like to think of 'is mill being lived in——'

'*Lived* in?'

Rachel felt a sharp pain in her palm, and found the teeth of the comb biting into it. When she looked up, the grey-green eyes had lengthened in a cozening stare.

'You do not know? Ned do not tell you 'ow 'e wish to 'ave it as a second 'ome?'

Worse and worse. So Ned was planning a second home—for a second woman? The hateful thought brought a red mist before Rachel's eyes, and the feeling that her head was suddenly a long way from her body.

'It will take time to make right,' the girl added. 'Years, 'e think.'

And who knew what would happen in those years? Who knew what a fully mature Claudette would coax Ned to? Already, while little more than a schoolgirl, she had persuaded him to make love to her.

And now he tells her plans he's never mentioned to me, Rachel fumed amid that swirling red mist. What else can it mean but that she's included in them, and I'm not?

It was all too easy to imagine how it would work out. And the Greniers would see that Ned did the right thing by their daughter—hadn't they already trained her to be a good wife? No doubt the valeting of a suit was the least of her skills.

'I suppose you can cook, too?' Rachel exclaimed, hardly aware of what she was saying. 'All that delicious French food?'

'Cook?' The smooth forehead wrinkled in bewilderment. 'We speak of cooking?'

'Can you?'

'*Maman* make me learn, yes...'

Rachel slammed her comb and brush into the suitcase. 'So you only need time to grow up a little.'

And I'm not hanging about for that, she added to herself. From today on, Ned Flavell is up for grabs. I've done with him.

If she said it often enough, she might start to mean it.

'Oh, but I am grown-up now,' Claudette was assuring her. 'After last night, I wish for no more trouble...'

She leapt like a guilty gazelle, then listened in strained silence. The springy footsteps hurrying up the stairs could only belong to one person. Rachel straightened from the suitcase, and was distantly aware of Claudette snatching the jacket into half-concealment behind her back as the door flew open.

'Come on down, Jel, I want you...oh.' Ned paused on the threshold, bright hair on end with the speed of his passage, steely glance settling on Claudette and staying there.

He hardly sees me, Rachel thought, trying to get used to the hurt of it. He only has eyes for *her*.

Claudette, however, didn't seem to appreciate the attention. She kept the jacket uncomfortably clutched to her back, and took one small, tentative step to the door.

'Please,' she quavered, 'I...I will go now.'

'Stay where you are,' Ned ordered, and crossed to the street-facing window. 'Keep her here, Jel,' he called over his shoulder.

'What?' Rachel could hardly believe her ears. 'You expect *me* to look after your mistress...?'

'My *what*?' He turned from the half-open window to stare at her. 'Do you know what you're saying?'

'Don't I just!' She prepared to tell him exactly what she thought of him. 'For the first time in my life, maybe...'

She broke off, startled by a rush of movement past her. Claudette whisked out of the door, banged it after her, and scurried down the stairs.

'Now look what you've done. Oh, well.' Ned pushed the casement the rest of the way open. 'She won't get far.'

And that was all the time he had to spare for Rachel. He was now leaning out of the window, bawling down at the street in tones a racecourse tout might envy.

'She's on her way down,' he bawled. 'Come on up, and bring her with you.'

'Who are you ordering about this time?' Rachel demanded, and crossed to see for herself. 'Don't close it...'

'Keep your hair on.' He left the casement open, the heady perfumes of a southern May, of roses and honeysuckle and lilac, blowing in to mingle with his own scent of lemon.

'Stand away,' she snapped, holding off from him. 'How can I see out if you're stuck there like a...' she cast round for inspiration '...like a blasted wardrobe?'

'Who are you calling a wardrobe?' And he drew her close, his arms folding her tight. 'Now if you'd said a trouser-press——'

'Leave me alone, you two-timing bastard!'

But she might as well not have spoken. His lips came down on hers, and the old magic worked as strong as ever. She had to return his kiss, had to savour the hardness of his mouth and the lean strength of his body, if only for this one, last time.

'You needn't think that'll make any difference,' she panted as soon as he let her speak, and tried to push him away. 'I'm leaving you, Ned Flavell. The minute you stop mauling me——'

'Then I'll keep hold.' And he did, with a grip like warm iron. 'Mauling you indeed,' he added, belatedly indignant. 'And what's this rubbish about leaving me? Do you really think you can spend the rest of your life alone?'

'There you go again, you...*troglodyte*,' she burst out, as helpless against his cool superiority as she was against his iron muscles. 'As if there weren't a hundred better men for me to meet the minute I get clear of you.'

'None of them fathered your baby.'

'*What* baby? Isn't that typical of you?' She ceased her struggles in triumph at this new ammunition. 'You've decided you want a family, so we have to have started one first go.'

'Dammit, I only said——'

'I heard what you said. And you'd better be wrong.' She turned her head away, unable to be this near him without wanting him to kiss her again. 'The last thing I need now,' she went on, as much for herself as for him, 'is to be pregnant by an arrogant, inconsiderate, scheming——'

'Calm down, Jel.' He gave her a little shake. 'Try and start making sense, will you?'

'I'm making it. At last.' She took a deep breath, and another, to show how calm she was. 'At last I'm seeing you clear, Ned Flavell. I wonder how many other women you've had?'

'For heaven's sake!' He heaved a great sigh, a haloed saint infinitely put upon. 'Do we have to go on with all this?'

'I suppose you've no idea what I'm on about?'

'Wrong again; I've a pretty good idea...'

He stopped, bright head tilted to one side. Far off down the staircase, amplified by the stairwell, Claudette's voice rose in noisy dispute with a deeper one which had to be a man's.

'Have you noticed,' Ned began conversationally, 'that special way the French shout when they're arguing?'

He spoke with such amiable interest that they might have been friends. He had even relaxed his grip, so sure was he that she wouldn't get away. Outside the noise grew louder. Pounding, slightly uneven footsteps mounted the stairs.

'They hit one particular high note,' he went on, 'and stay there...' He stopped as the door burst open on a flailing mass of arms and legs. 'Well done, Étienne!'

Étienne nodded and grinned in the doorway, the kicking Claudette slung over his shoulder. Her neat little rump stuck up by his ear, and he had her legs firmly pinned to his chest so that none of her kicks did him any harm.

'You can't do that!' Rachel gasped in horror. 'What is this—a kidnapping?'

'All in good time, Jel. Hold her!' Ned reached the door, panther-swift, and flung it wide.

'*Merci, patron.*'

Étienne staggered in and dropped Ned's jacket to the bed. Then, with sheer male delight in his own ruffianly strength, he did a twirling dance step with Claudette still over his shoulder. Her hairband had come off; heavy strands of dark gold hair hid her face, but didn't stop her hammering uselessly at his back. From under the tangled hair poured a stream of what must surely be abuse, all, as Ned had observed, on one high, continuous note.

'Put her down at once!' Rachel exclaimed. 'This is sheer...brutality!'

'You ain't seen nothin' yet.' Ned turned the key in the lock, removed it, and dropped it into his trouser pocket. 'Now,' he ordered, 'let's be having her.'

'She will scream,' Étienne pointed out. 'Better you close the window as well.'

'If she meant to scream she'd have done it long ago,' Rachel snapped. 'You're just putting off letting her go. How dare you treat a woman like this——?'

'Lay off, Jel. But she's right about the screaming; I don't think it need worry us.' Ned strolled into the centre of the room, his height and his air of command giving him immediate control of it. 'Just put her down, so we can get on.'

Étienne obeyed, sliding Claudette down and setting her on her feet. For a moment she stayed close to him, coral-tipped fingers pushing her hair back to show wide eyes full of...

It can't be, Rachel thought. She can't really be looking at the man who's treated her like this with such...admiration?

But it was more than admiration which shone from the grey-green eyes. The girl lowered her lashes and turned away, sitting on the end of the bed where Ned gestured her, but her secret was still there in every line of her body. Though she sat with head bowed, face once more hidden in the curtains of dark gold hair, she could no longer hide it.

She loves Étienne, Rachel thought. She's as much in his power as I am in...as I *used to be* in...

'Now, then.' Ned sat astride a chair, arms along its back. 'Sit down, Étienne, and we can begin.'

Rachel watched with fury as the other man obediently settled in the one remaining chair. So she was meant to stand, was she? Or perhaps she should sit where these lords of creation no doubt felt she belonged, at their feet?

'Right!' she murmured half under her breath.

With defiant slowness, she sauntered to the bed and sat down by Claudette. The girl emerged from her swaths of hair for an astonished stare, which quickly turned to gratitude as she understood she had an ally. Then she hid again, and left Rachel to be brave for both.

'OK, Jel, if that's what you want.' Ned's tone was indulgent, if a little puzzled. 'But she hasn't been much of a friend to you, has she?'

'She's only a child,' Rachel snapped. 'You've absolutely no right to manhandle and humiliate her——'

'Leave it, or we'll never get this done. Now, Claudette——' he settled to business '—we're going to sort out all these lies you've been spinning. Let's start with what you told my girl.'

The only reply was a frozen, absolute stillness. Rachel could feel it next to her, the stillness of a wild creature hiding from its hunters. Seconds passed.

'I will tell you,' Étienne answered at last. 'I 'ad it all from 'er a moment ago...'

And he began. As she listened, Rachel grew almost as still as the girl beside her. The attitudes of the two men, the tones of their voices, their every movement radiated such contempt for what Ned had called 'these lies' that she almost began to feel ashamed of ever having believed them. How could she have taken seriously this stuff about love in the afternoon, on a bed of moss...?

'But the moss was all flattened,' she protested. 'And your jacket, Ned...'

He silenced her with a gesture, and turned to his henchman. 'Where does my jacket come into this?'

'She took it from 'er father's car yesterday, and spread it over the moss to sunbathe. I found 'er there——' with a brief, Gallic flick of dark eyes on the bowed victim '—and I tell you, *monsieur*, I was tempted. If it were not for 'er father...' The dark eyes snapped back to attention. 'Also, I did not know that it was *monsieur*'s suit she was destroying.'

'Forget the suit,' Ned growled. 'Claudette, have I ever touched you except to get rid of you?'

Another long pause, and then the dark gold hair swung to and fro in silent, reluctant denial.

Rachel stared sideways at it, strangely light-headed. 'No *cinq-à-sept*?' she asked, just to be sure. 'No home for the two of you in the old water-mill?'

'No what?' Ned roared.

The chair rattled to the carpet and lay there as he leapt to his feet. In one stride he had reached the two of them and was standing over the terrified girl. Seen from below, his chin was rock-hard, his mouth cruelly straight, his eyes slits of fury.

'Is that what you've been saying?'

'I 'ave not! I would nevaire...'

Claudette's wail choked into full-scale sobs. When she shook back her hair, strands of it stayed plastered to her cheeks, soaked with tears, and fresh tears poured from her beautiful eyes.

''ow could I evaire say such things?' she pleaded. 'I told of the mill, but not that I was to live in it with you!' Agitated once more, she scrubbed at her wet cheeks with inelegant knuckles. 'If *Maman* should 'ear this, she would lock me in my room——'

'Just what you need, you little blabbermouth. Where did you hear I'm after the mill?'

'Stop booming at her.' Rachel put an arm round the trembling shoulders. 'Can't you see you're frightening the child?'

Ned blinked, then turned on her with an astonishment that almost made her smile. He looked as if his favourite dog had suddenly talked back.

'I'm surprised at you sticking up for her, Jel.'

'All I'm doing——' she managed to bring it out strong and level '—is trying to make you behave. It's *wrong*——' she gave the word all the force she could summon '—for a man to terrorise a woman by brute strength. Now back off, will you?'

For a moment they might have been alone in the room. She raised her chin and let their glances lock. If she lost this one, something vital would be gone, something in the very fabric which kept them together. She had to win—she knew it deep within her—because she was right and he was wrong.

And he knew it too, she saw with relief. In their battle of the eyes he was the first to yield, dropping his gaze with a barely audible sigh. When he raised it again it was still hard, but the menace had gone from it.

'Are you taking over from me, Jel?'

'Of course not.' The words rushed from her in a great breath of relief. 'Just pick up that chair and sit down...'

She broke off with a gasp, knowing she had gone too far. How dared she give him orders like this? She wasn't surprised when he turned from her, walked right on past the overturned chair, and planted himself in front of the garden-facing window, a huge figure against the brilliance of high morning.

'So where do we go from here?' he demanded with deliberate calm. 'How do you propose to get the truth out of her, Jel?'

'By asking, of course.' She patted the slender shoulder next to hers, and noted that it had stopped shaking. 'Tell us where you heard about the mill, Claudette.'

The only reply was a loud, manufactured sob.

'You see?' Étienne began. 'Now she uses your pity...'

Ned gestured him to silence, his eyes on Rachel. 'How do we deal with this one, Jel?'

He really meant it, she realised, and felt a newer, deeper, rejoicing love for him wash through her.

He wasn't trying to put her down for having stopped him frightening Claudette. He really had understood about that, and now wanted her advice and help as from one friend to another. And because of his trust and support she knew exactly what to do. She turned to the girl beside her.

'Don't milk it, my dear.' Feeling infinitely the older and wiser, she brushed back the wet hair. 'Just get this over with.'

The first response was a baleful stare. Rachel met it with wry amusement—the brat was bound to be annoyed rather than grateful. She smiled across at Ned, sharing the joke, and presently Claudette's hair swung over her face in admitted guilt.

'Maître Gérard, he tell Papa. I listen at the door.'

Ned gave Rachel a nod of satisfaction, but did not speak. The silence was broken only by Étienne, who clicked his tongue and shook his head. Claudette turned to him like a scolded pet, and from there it seemed natural for him to take up the questioning.

'And now we return to the other matter. It is understood, Claudette, that you couched with neither of us?'

'Neither of you?' Rachel glanced up at the stern dark eyes. 'She lied about you as well?'

'Very seriously, *madame*.'

'To me,' Ned put in from his place by the window.

'To my future *employeur*,' Étienne added, dark eyes flashing. 'She abused my name to the man on 'oom my career depends——'

'You see the problem?' Ned's cooler voice took over. 'I didn't believe her yarn, but that moss fitted so well . . .'

'Just as it fitted what she told me,' Rachel agreed. 'She must have dreamed it up while she was sunbathing.'

'It did fit, didn't it?' He considered the new idea. 'So while I was sorting things out with Étienne you were convinced you'd learnt the worst about me?'

'S-something like that.' Now it was Rachel's turn to look down, ashamed to have been so taken in. 'She had the jacket, and the news about the mill which you hadn't even told me . . .'

'My poor Jel.' His voice sharpened. 'Have you anything to say for yourself, Claudette?'

No answer.

'You made trouble between me and my . . . my woman——' a warmth crept into his voice as he used the word '—and that's bad. But what if your father had heard your story about Étienne? Would he have believed it?'

''e would 'ave, *monsieur*,' Étienne answered after another wait. 'For various unimportant reasons——' a movement from the girl brought the dark eyes to her with a gaze both smouldering and repressive '—'e would 'ave. And then, 'e would certainly not 'ave sold me the wine I need in my restaurant.'

'*Your* restaurant?' Rachel queried, lost again.

'Soon I will manage the Castaire restaurant for a trial period,' Étienne explained with quiet pride. 'Then, per'aps——'

'Then we'll see,' Ned interrupted decisively, and turned to Rachel. 'He just might——' with a quelling glance at Étienne '—be the man to look after things for me while I'm busy here.'

'When I am on the board of Flavell Enterprises,' Étienne announced, 'then per'aps Monsieur Grenier will think again about whether I am worthy of 'is daughter.'

'You'd marry her?' Rachel asked, so intrigued that she hardly noticed the sudden fire-cracker noises from Claudette. 'After all the trouble she's made?'

''e will *not*,' the girl spat out in a fury. 'Nevaire, nevaire, nevaire! Not if 'e were the richest...'

She switched to furious, high-speed French. Étienne shrugged, and ignored it to answer Rachel.

'You see, *madame*, 'ow young she is? She will learn.'

Rachel nodded, recalling how she had hated Ned—was it really only minutes ago? So much had happened since that it felt like a lifetime.

'*Madame, monsieur.*' Étienne rose to his feet. 'I think we 'ave taken enough of your time. Come, Claudette.'

He offered a hand to the still-fizzing girl. She bridled, glared at it, and stopped in mid-flow. Reluctantly, as if she couldn't help herself, she took it and rose to let him lead her to the door. Only there did she pause.

'Ze jacket!' She darted back to where it lay draped over the suitcase. 'I 'ave said I will make it like new.'

'Oh, but there's no need,' Rachel began. 'He has...'

The briefest movement from Ned—a mere turn of the head—was enough to silence her. Étienne made a final courtly bow, and closed the door. Beyond it, Claudette's voice at once rose anew, and continued protesting all the way down the stairs.

'Why make her press your jacket,' Rachel asked from her place on the bed, 'when you've got another suit with you?'

'She messed it up, didn't she? Tidying it's the least she can do.' He stayed by the window, distant and forbidding. 'So you really believed I'd... What the hell got into you?'

'I told you,' Rachel explained again. 'The moss, the jacket, it all seemed to f-fit...' She stammered to a halt, dismayed by the angry tilt of his gold-glinting head.

'Not that, the other thing. Dammit, Jel, I wouldn't give Claudette Grenier the time of day!' Still separated from her by the May-scented breadth of the room, he glared in righteous wrath. 'Let alone my mill to live in.'

'I... I didn't really think that——'

'To dream up such a thing.' Her denial washed off him like water from a stone. 'And all by yourself, without even any lies from Claudette to help. Why, you're nearly as bad as she is...'

'What?' Rachel hardly believed her ears, or her eyes when she saw him shake his saintly, martyred head.

'Don't you know me at all, Rachel Barclay?'

'I didn't, but I'm starting to, Nathan Flavell,' she retorted on a strengthening wave of anger. 'And I don't like everything I'm finding out, either.'

'And what's that supposed to mean?' he demanded, still long-suffering. 'What's come over you this time?'

'It has to be something come over me, doesn't it?' She shot upright, the better to deal with her racing thoughts. 'It couldn't be you who's done something wrong, could it?' She saw him about to answer and swept on, talking him down. 'Because you've never done anything wrong in all your life, have you?'

'I certainly haven't in this case——'

'Or only the usual. Treat 'em rough and tell 'em nothing—that's how you think you can deal with women——'

'Where the hell did you get that idea?'

'What you should be asking is why it took me so long to find it out.' She crossed to face him in the brilliant morning light. 'Goodness knows, your mother's told me often enough.'

'Oh, if you listen to *her*——'

'I shouldn't, should I? She's only a woman, and nobody ever listens to women. Women,' Rachel rushed on, determined to finish before he could stop her, 'never make any sense, do they?'

'You're certainly not making any now.' He seemed unrepentant—yet could that be a hint of doubt in the steely eyes? 'Just what am I supposed to have done?'

'Only the usual,' she repeated, grabbing her advantage. 'Made plans involving me...' She stopped on a new, painful idea. 'I suppose your plans for the mill do involve me?'

'Of course they do!' He stuffed his hands in his pockets and turned to stare unseeingly out of the window. 'You and whatever family we have—*when* we have one.' His furious sideways glance showed he hadn't forgotten her earlier accusations. 'We're...we *were*——' another furious glance '—all going to live in it, as soon as I could make it habitable.'

'Thanks.' She put all her recent bitterness into the mocking formality. 'And I had to hear about it by common gossip.'

'That little snake! I'll wring her neck...' He trailed off, realising as well as Rachel did that this wasn't the point.

She brought him back to it. 'Why didn't you tell me, Ned?'

'I was going to, as soon as the deal was settled...' He tried again. 'I knew you'd be as keen on the place as I am...' Another pause, the tip of his tongue caught between his teeth in that way it had when he was thinking something out.

At the sight of that thoughtful tongue, a wave of love washed over Rachel. She mustn't weaken, she told herself, but all the same her next question came out much gentler.

'The way I was keen on what you planned for us last night? Which you also,' she reminded him, 'organised without asking me.'

In the brilliant light, the steel-blue eyes met hers with difficult honesty. She waited, breathless, sending all her silent will to help him. He must meet this new challenge as he had met so many others, with the courage to do what he knew should be done.

And he did, though he almost gagged on the irksome, little-used words. 'I'm...I'm sorry, Jel.'

She wanted to fling herself into his arms, to cover every one of those hard, loved features with kisses. She actually took a step towards him, and had to rein herself back.

'Sorry for what, exactly?' she managed, inches away from him.

'For not telling you...' Another pause, shamefaced. 'For not *asking* you. Either about that room, or about the mill.'

Could she really stay apart from him for a moment longer? Yet she must, until the job was finished. She closed her eyes and dug her nails into her palms to control the love which would have driven her to him.

'I don't mind any more about the room, my darling. But the mill...tell me about it now.'

And he did. How he'd come across the place while exploring the town before she arrived. How he'd sought out the old lawyer who owned it, and made an offer. How the final price was not yet fixed, but the terms were emerging ever clearer.

'Claudette said you planned it for a second home,' she put in presently.

'Trust her to get it wrong,' he retorted with a return of his usual force. 'Maître Gérard won't have that. But for a family to live in, all the year round...' He broke off, sighing. 'For that, I'd have been in with a chance.'

'*Would* have been? You mean,' Rachel asked carefully, 'you'll give up the idea if I don't like it?'

He stared at her. 'You don't think I'd trade *you* for a building, do you? If,' he added with newly learnt doubt, 'I've still got you. Have I, Jel?'

'We haven't finished about the mill.' She put her hands behind her back, to stop them reaching out for him. 'Supposing you get it liveable, and comfortable——'

'I'd do that all right,' he interrupted. 'I know exactly where the master bedroom's going to be, and the nurseries——'

'So it wouldn't take you long?'

'Two years at most. We could be living in it after one.'

'And then what?'

'There'll still be lots to do on it.'

'And you'll do it. And then what?'

He shrugged, and turned away from her to stare out of the window. Rachel refused to be put off by the impatient angle of the eagle profile.

'You've a lot of years ahead yet,' she pointed out gently. 'Plenty of time to be bored again, as you are now with Flavell's.'

'I never will.' He faced her once more. 'Not if I have you.'

'You've had me for two years,' she made herself say. 'More. I've been with you all my life, really.'

'Not as you are now. Something's happened to you, Jel.' The thoughtful tongue showed again between the even teeth. 'Last night, when you were so good with Claudette after the crash——'

'Was I?' She cast her mind back, wondering how.

'I knew then that you were right about it being time to start a family. Knew that I...' he looked down, embarrassed, at the forest-scuffed tip of his polished shoe '...that I wanted your children to be mine.'

'So *that's* why you changed your mind so suddenly.' She paused, not wanting to reproach him further, yet knowing she must. 'You should have told me, you know.'

'I know. That kind of stuff doesn't come easy to me——' he raised his head with sudden resolution '—so, as I've started, I'll keep on.' The steely eyes met and held hers. 'Funny, it was Claudette again...you did such a great job on her just now...'

'I did?' Rachel recalled her defiance of the men, and her rebuke to Ned. 'I know I was angry with you both, and that made me sympathise with her, but——'

'It made me see how you'd be with our daughters. And that's when I knew——' his old decisiveness surged back '—I had to have you for good. If,' he added on careful second thoughts, 'you'll let me. Will you let me, Jel?'

Oh, yes, Ned, she wanted to shout, yes and yes and yes. Her throat almost hurt with the effort of holding it back, of keeping her voice down, of setting this final test which he must pass.

'I…I'm not sure I want to leave Caster. Could you…' she struggled to get it out '…could you bear to stay there?'

For a long time, he didn't answer. Then he turned again to the window, gazed out at the sunny sky as at departing dreams, heaved a great sigh, faced her once more.

'I suppose I can always go on managing Flavell's. And we might find some other mill——'

'No need for that,' she cut in. 'I love the idea of this one as much as you do.'

He frowned. 'So why say you want to stay in Caster?'

'Just testing, Ned.'

'Why, you little…'

And at last she was in his arms. At long last she could cling to him, offer him her lips and her love and her body and her life, and know they were in safe keeping. And as if the release of her love had filled her with new power she knew also the solution to the problem that had been worrying her.

'About what you'd do once we're living in the mill.' She turned aside one of his kisses, and summoned all her new strength to go on. 'Have you thought of restoring the machinery? Grinding flour again?'

He had transferred the kiss to her cheek, and from there to her ear. Now he stopped abruptly and pulled her round to face him, drawing away from her so that he could stare down at her with blazing eyes.

'Jel, you're a genius.' He let her go, opened the window, and proclaimed it across the garden. 'I'm in love with a genius!'

'Come in, you idiot!' She fluttered between him and the window. 'Maître Gérard won't sell to somebody he thinks is mad.'

'Yes, he will. He'd sell to Lucifer——' Ned scooped her into his arms, and whirled her in a dance of triumph '—if Lucifer promised to get his beloved mill back to working order.'

She clung to him, dizzy with happiness and his swift movements. 'It'll take you years...'

'I'll scour Europe for parts, or have them made.' As he spoke, he carried her to the bed. 'I'll make it a show-place, part of the green revolution. They'll bring their grain for miles...'

He stopped abruptly, and set her on her feet. When she looked round for the cause of his change of mood, she found it was the half-packed suitcase.

'You really did mean to go, didn't you?'

'So would you,' she countered, closing the suitcase, 'if you found I'd—er—couched with Étienne, for instance.'

'I would not. Well, anyway——' he picked up the suitcase as if it were a toy, and flung it rattling across the room '—not till I'd broken his neck. And very likely yours, too.'

'There you go again. So...so *physical*!'

'You like me physical.'

'Up to a point. A very nice point, mind you... What are you doing?' she demanded through the robin-red T-shirt, as he slid it over her head. 'That's the second time you've had this off me in...how many hours?' She emerged from its folds to glance at his travelling clock. 'When are you seeing Maître Gérard?'

'Late this afternoon,' he murmured, his mouth busy with her shoulders. 'We can make it.'

'Make what?' she gasped as his lips settled in the hollow of her throat.

'Whatever you want, my darling.'

'Marriage vows?'

'You bet. As soon as we can fix it.'

She put a hand to his crumpled, yesterday's shirt, and found its buttons unaccountably unfastened. Her fingers slid within it, pushing it away to savour the hard breadth of his chest.

'Our folks'll want a wedding party...' She watched the shirt drop to the floor, and noted with surprise that her own trousers were now loose and sliding away from her. 'You'll have to tell me some time how you do this thing with fastenings.'

'I'll tell you anything you want to know, my darling.' He lifted her to the bed. 'Any time.'

'Some hope!' She moved sensuously under his hands, helping him with the rest of her clothes.

'I'm serious, my love. From now on, I'm telling you everything.' He leant over her, holding her gaze. 'That's a promise, and I'll hold to it.'

'Oh, Ned——' she flung her arms round his neck '—I do love you... What are we going to do about lunch?'

'Damn lunch.'

'That's all very well, but——'

'Stop talking.'

'Yes, Ned.'

And she did, until many hours later. Then, sleepy and content, she lay in his arms and watched two tortoiseshell butterflies chase each other back and forth through the warmth of late noon.

'I suppose it's time we stirred ourselves...'

'Not yet.' He stroked her hair, and then her shoulder, and then her breast. 'Not till I've...' He stopped speaking, and let his body say the rest.

'Oh, my goodness,' she murmured as she yielded to him once more. 'I wonder if the bridal-wear shops sell maternity dresses?'

PENNY JORDAN

A COLLECTION

Volume 2

From the bestselling author of *Power Play*, *The Hidden Years* and *Lingering Shadows* comes a second collection of three sensuous love stories, beautifully presented in one special volume.

Featuring:

FIRE WITH FIRE
CAPABLE OF FEELING
SUBSTITUTE LOVER

Available from May 1993   Priced: £4.99

W⦿RLDWIDE

Another Face . . .
Another Identity . . .
Another Chance . . .

When her teenage love turns to hate, Geraldine Frances vows to even the score. After arranging her own "death", she embarks on a dramatic transformation emerging as *Silver,* a hauntingly beautiful and mysterious woman few men would be able to resist.

With a new face and a new identity, she is now ready to destroy the man responsible for her tragic past.

Silver – a life ruled by one all-consuming passion, is Penny Jordan at her very best.

WORLDWIDE

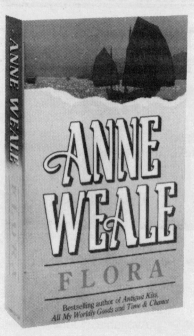

Mills & Boon

Forthcoming Titles

BEST SELLER ROMANCE
Available in June

AN AWAKENING DESIRE Helen Bianchin
WHIRLWIND Charlotte Lamb

DUET
Available in June

The Carole Mortimer Duet   **VELVET PROMISE**
                                    TANGLED HEARTS

The Sally Wentworth Duet   **MISTAKEN WEDDING**
                                    SATAN'S ISLAND

MEDICAL ROMANCE
Available in June

A BORDER PRACTICE Drusilla Douglas
A SONG FOR DR ROSE Margaret Holt
THE LAST EDEN Marion Lennox
HANDFUL OF DREAMS Margaret O'Neill

Available from Boots, Martins, John Menzies, W.H. Smith,
most supermarkets and other paperback stockists.

Also available from Mills & Boon Reader Service,
Freepost, P.O. Box 236, Thornton Road, Croydon,
Surrey CR9 9EL.

Readers in South Africa - write to:
Book Services International Ltd, P.O. Box 41654,
Craighall, Transvaal 2024.

June.

Next Month's Romances

Each month you can choose from a wide variety of romance with
Mills & Boon. Below are the new titles to look out for next month,
why not ask either Mills & Boon Reader Service or your
Newsagent to reserve you a copy of the titles you want to buy —
just tick the titles you would like and either post to Reader Service
or take it to any Newsagent and ask them to order your books.

all of them would like

Please save me the following titles:		Please tick	√
PARADISE LOST	Robyn Donald		
SNOWFIRE	Anne Mather		
A GIRL IN A MILLION	Betty Neels		√
HOUSE OF GLASS	Michelle Reid		
MASTER OF PASSION	Jacqueline Baird		√
DARK SUNLIGHT	Patricia Wilson		
ECHOES OF LOVE	Jeanne Allan		
ALL IT TAKES IS LOVE	Rosemary Hammond		
SATAN'S CONTRACT	Susanne McCarthy		
TOUCHED BY DESIRE	Lynsey Stevens		
COLD FIRE	Helen Brooks		√
UNWANTED LEGACY	Rachel Elliot		
DANCING WITH SHADOWS	Rosemary Badger		
HOLD BACK THE DARK	Jane Donnelly		
DRIVEN BY LOVE	Kristy McCallum		
GARDEN OF DESIRE	Laura Martin		

If you would like to order these books in addition to your regular
subscription from Mills & Boon Reader Service please send
£1.80 per title to: Mills & Boon Reader Service, Freepost, P.O.
Box 236, Croydon, Surrey, CR9 9EL, quote your Subscriber
No:................................... (If applicable) and complete the name
and address details below. Alternatively, these books are available
from many local Newsagents including W.H.Smith, J.Menzies,
Martins and other paperback stockists from 11th June 1993.

Name:...

Address:..

....Post Code:.........................

To Retailer: If you would like to stock M&B books please
contact your regular book/magazine wholesaler for details.